The T.O.P.*
Workbook for
Sexual Health
*Trauma Outcome Process

Joann Schladale

Resources For Resolving Violence, Inc.

The *T.O.P.* Workbook for Sexual Health* is a way to explore sexual decision-making. The Trauma Outcome Process simplifies how painful life experiences impact thoughts, feelings, physiological reactions, and behavior. It promotes healthy choices that celebrate sexuality.

This workbook is lovingly dedicated to my sister, Gayle, who had an illegal abortion on her 21st birthday.

And to Alexis who is working hard to learn about sexual health after experiencing trauma in her young life.

Special thanks are given to Triste and Lawrence Brooks who work tirelessly to prevent sexual harm. Without Triste's vision and leadership this workbook might not have been written.

The *National Campaign To Prevent Teen and Unplanned Pregnancy* generously provided grant funding for this project and 'Team Empower' have been delightful to work with. They are Cory Neering, Kimberly Sovinski, Kelly Chevalier, Susan and Ashley Philliber, Rosalind Brown, David Block, Kimberly Eardley, Cortina Peters, Lawrence Brooks, Jeff DeMario, and Wayne Pawlowski.

Heartfelt gratitude goes to Therese Langan who graciously reads everything I write, and makes me a better writer.

Most importantly, John's love and support sustain me throughout the creative process.

Table of Contents

Celebrating Sexuality!

Sexual health is "a state of physical, emotional, mental and social well-being in relation to sexuality; it is not merely the absence of disease, dysfunction or infirmity. Sexual health requires a positive and respectful approach to sexuality and sexual relationships, as well as the possibility of having pleasurable and safe sexual experiences, free of coercion, discrimination and violence. For sexual health to be attained and maintained, the sexual rights of all persons must be respected, protected and fulfilled."

— The World Health Organization

Sexuality is seldom treated as a strong or healthy force in the positive development of a child's personality in the United States.

— Floyd Martinson

Welcome to the T.O.P.* Workbook for Sexual Health. T.O.P.* stands for Trauma Outcome Process. *Trauma means bad things that have a lasting effect on your life. Outcome is a result, or consequence. A process is a particular way of doing something.* Your trauma outcome process is the way you choose to deal with very bad things that happened to you.

Sexual health, as you can see in the quote from the World Health Organization, represents all the ways you can embrace and celebrate your sexuality. Sexual health is not just practicing 'safer sex'. It is all about learning to take good care of yourself sexually in order to pursue your dreams and become the person you want to be. There's more about that later in the workbook. For now, it's just important to know that sexual health plays a big part in your overall health. Physical health and mental health work together to promote happiness and well-being. Even when people experience trauma there are many ways to celebrate sexual health.

Top 10 Reasons For This Workbook

1. To experience love!
2. To celebrate sexuality!
3. To take good care of yourself.
4. To reduce confusion.
5. To learn how to manage problems without causing harm to yourself and/or others.
6. To heal pain.
7. To prevent unplanned or unwanted pregnancy.
8. To help you pursue your dreams!
9. To explore becoming the person you really want to be!
10. To have a lot more fun in life!

Young people get a lot of messages about sexuality. These messages come from television, movies, the Internet, video games, families, friends, teachers, and other people in your community. Unfortunately, many of these are mixed messages and do not promote sexual health. Sexual messages and practices that do not promote sexual health can cause harm.

These terms will be explained in a lot more detail later in the workbook. Right now you can get started by just reading a bit to help you get comfortable with the information.

Chapter One:
So Many Choices!

This workbook was created for a lot of reasons. The most important reasons are to help you experience well-being. *Well-being is the state of being comfortable, healthy, or happy.* There are a lot of choices to make when it comes to sexual health and well-being! Everyone has sexual confusion at different times in life, particularly during adolescence. Deciding what makes us happy can be quite a challenge! Making sense of all the choices can promote health and well-being.

Deciding to be healthy means taking a stand against all the messages, and temptations that get in the way of good decision-making. This is extra hard when life has been rough. Sometimes pain from your past creates more problems. Such problems might keep you from taking good care of yourself and becoming the person you really want to be. They can get in the way of your dreams. Extra problems get in the way of having fun and enjoying life. This workbook provides an opportunity to change your way of thinking about your past and reduce problems in the present and future.

You might be wondering why you should bother with this workbook. Some young people don't see any point in focusing on success. Unnecessary problems can serve a purpose. They might get other people's attention. They provide drama when you're bored. You might think they'll get people to leave you alone. They might make others afraid of you. They can even be sensational and invite media attention. You might not believe anything can change to make things better in your life. You might believe that by ignoring pain in your life it will

> Jamie is a young woman who grew up in the foster care system. She and her sister were removed from home after being sexually abused by some of her mom's friends. Jamie struggled with eating disorders and was hospitalized twice. One foster mother was an alcoholic so Jamie and her sister had to live in two different group homes because no other foster families were available. She wasn't a great student but she got a job in a local grocery store after school and was able to keep up with her studies. When Jamie was 17 she wanted to begin having sex with her boyfriend and spoke with her state worker and therapist about it. Since it seemed the easiest, she decided to have Depo Provera shots so she wouldn't get pregnant. Jamie is now living with family friends, dating, and enjoying life.

Top 10 Reasons for Choosing Health and Well-Being

1. Safety!
2. Success!
3. Enjoyment!
4. Affection!
5. Love!
6. Power!
7. Control!
8. Health!
9. Fun!
10. Celebrating yourself!

go away. You may also think that people wanting to help have nothing of value to give you.

Trouble from the past can be hard to deal with! You may think you have to give up some things you don't want to when you decide to get rid of problems. There are pros and cons to consider when healing pain. There are a lot of choices to make along the way. They are decisions only you can make. No one can force you to make them. Take your time to think about the different things that play a part in healing pain.

By learning to heal pain you can focus on taking good care of yourself and becoming the person you really want to be. When you manage problems without causing harm to yourself, or others, you have a lot more time to focus on your dreams. Consider following your dreams. You can do it! Even when really bad things have happened, hopes and dreams can survive. It may be hard, but change is possible.

This workbook was also created to help make your life easier. Young people receive some confusing messages about sexual health. Movies and television might make you think that drugs, violence, and sexual aggression are cool. *Aggression is forceful, attacking behavior*. If you see aggression being rewarded you might think it's okay. Power that comes from aggression is bad. It is abusive. Aggression causes pain. This workbook was written to help you figure out ways to ease pain in your life. You can do this by slowing down and taking time to make sense of any confusion.

Learning about sexual health can help you be clear about your needs and wants. It can help you learn to assert yourself in order to take good care of yourself sexually. *Assert means to communicate confidently*. You can learn to be assertive and take good care of yourself.

Young people who have experienced harm often share stories about feeling powerless when others behave aggressively. Some were treated badly and often felt isolated and alone. Experiencing violence can influence a desire for revenge. *Revenge is hurting someone for something mean they did to you*. It can cause confusion and put young people at risk of shameful and disgraceful behavior. Violence can also cause hopelessness, and put youth at risk of being abused.

When bad things happen it might be hard to make sense of them. When adults aren't there to help, children struggle with things alone. Some young people who have been hurt avoid others and spend a lot of time alone. Sometimes being alone is good and helps people calm down. Too much time alone can make you feel lonely, and sometimes, scared. It can also make you think nobody cares, and nobody's trustworthy. You may not believe it, but many people are trustworthy. Making sense of pain can help you figure out how to gain well-being. It can help you learn about people you can trust and those you can't trust. It can help you learn how to enjoy being with people who help you feel good about yourself, and avoid those who cause pain. It can help you learn how to have a lot more fun in your life!

Connection

Connecting with other people is one of the most important things everyone does in life. When you consider health and well-being there are a lot of things to think about. You can't achieve them alone. A lot of people are happy to help you. They can support you in many ways. You may want to have someone with you as you answer questions in this workbook. You may want to work alone sometimes and meet with others to talk about the answers. Talking with others can help you figure out exactly how your answers to the questions can help you experience health and well-being.

This workbook can also help you learn to take good care of yourself. *Taking good care of yourself means protecting yourself, and others, from harm.* It is a way to learn about health and well-being. This means learning to prevent bad things from happening to you. It also means making sure you don't hurt yourself or others.

You may wonder why you should bother taking good care of yourself. You might also wonder why adults in your life didn't take better care of you. These are important questions! Questions like these come up all the time in life. They can be hard questions and you might be afraid of them. Making sense of such questions can help heal pain. When you consider taking good care of yourself think about how these questions might help you. You might want to think about the pros and cons of taking good care of yourself.

People Can Help You By:

1. Listening.
2. Having fun with you.
3. Getting to know you.
4. Coaching.
5. Teaching.
6. Mentoring.
7. Providing spiritual guidance.
8. Talking.
9. Sharing wisdom.
10. Giving comfort.

Patrick never talked about anything personal to anyone. He didn't see any point in talking. He was in a group home for almost a year before he decided to tell staff about his problems. When he finally did, he tried to cover up his fear by getting into a fight with staff. It took him a long time to realize staff was not there to hurt him and that he could tell others what was going on without causing harm.

Change

People are constantly changing. Our bodies and minds mature and change daily. As you grow you develop a broad range of skills and talent to manage change. You may have noticed you're good at something like schoolwork, art, or sports. Being good at something can help you build confidence, and confidence helps people deal with change. As you consider choices and changes you may want to make about your health and well-being think about how your skills and talents can help you along the way.

You might think nobody notices your talents, or the good things you do. So if you've tried to change some things, but others give you messages that the changes don't matter, or you're not good enough, it can be frustrating. You may wonder, what's the point? You might feel like you don't want to change, or you may be afraid of change. When you think of things you don't like about yourself, you may want to change. Sometimes you may feel like you don't have the power to make things change. You do!

When you think about reasons for this workbook, reasons for healing pain, and reasons for wanting to take good care of yourself, the reasons are all about choices and change. This whole workbook is about choices. Take your time to think about change. The more you think about it the more likely you will be to make healthy choices and lasting changes. Thinking about these things might also help you become clear about some dreams you have.

As soon as Dashia could get hold of drugs or alcohol she began using them to block out pain in her life. She saw her parents do the same thing so she thought it would work for her. What she didn't realize is that substance abuse doesn't heal pain. It just covers it up for a short time, and makes things worse in the long run.

Dashia never saw adults taking good care of themselves so she had no idea how to take good care of herself. She was used to people smoking, drinking, overeating, and doing dangerous things like fighting and driving recklessly. When she couldn't get any drugs, or alcohol, she learned how to manage pain differently. She learned how to heal painful experiences by daring to give up bad habits. She learned to accept pain so she could figure out where it was coming from and how to heal it. Unfortunately, others in her family were not successful. Her mother died from problems related to alcohol but Dashia continues to take good care of herself.

Stephen was a young man with disabilities and mental illness that caused him a lot of anger and frustration. He dreamed of graduating from high school and living on his own but he had to live in a group home. While he was there he was able to get medication for his illness and he was able to think about how he might make his life better. He studied to get his diploma and created a plan to get a place of his own. He was offered a job at a local discount store and began to put the plan into place.

Practice

This workbook has a lot of questions! The only way you can become the person you want to be is to figure out answers to many questions that come up in life. This takes practice. You may notice that a lot of the questions are alike. This is so you can successfully learn how to experience health and well-being.

The practice it takes to become the person you want to be is just like the practice it takes a baseball team to win the World Series. Every question you answer is like making a good catch or hitting the ball when you're at bat. It gives you practice to keep making more good catches and hitting more balls. Everybody who gets up to bat strikes out sometimes. All good catchers drop the ball sometimes. All players experience a slump when things aren't going well. This is like the challenge of making healthy choices. It takes constant practice that involves some home runs and some strike outs.

When you get to be a really good player you get to go to the Major Leagues. When you excel in the majors, you become an all-star and are recruited by the best teams. Even the most valuable players have to practice doing their best all the time. When you feel like a winner, you want to keep winning!

You may never play baseball, but you can still make great choices! You can win in the world series of life by making sense of what you need for health and well-being. You can take good care of yourself and create a plan to make your dreams come true. You can become the person you want to be!

When you are clear about your dreams, and figure out how to make them come true, you will understand how questions in this workbook can help. When you find questions frustrating, or challenging, talk to someone about them. You might ask someone you trust to explain how the questions might help you. You can ask others how they found them to be helpful. Feel free to add your own questions whenever you want to.

Now it's time to get started. There are no right or wrong answers to the questions. They are here to help you think clearly and to give you ideas about what you really want in life.

Top 10 Ways You Can Take Good Care of Yourself

1. Laugh as much as possible!
2. Cry when you need to.
3. Make good friends.
4. Speak your truth.
5. Exercise.
6. Don't smoke, drink, or do drugs.
7. Love!
8. Relax!
9. Meditate.
10. Have fun!

HEALTH AND WELL-BEING

Why should I bother thinking about health and well-being?

_____

_____

Why might I want to change anything about myself?

_____

_____

What good will it do to heal pain in my life?

_____

_____

When am I enjoying health and well-being?

_____

_____

Who cares whether I'm healthy?

_____

_____

Who might I look up to as a model for health and well-being?

_____

_____

Who might I talk to about these things?

_____

_____

Dreams

Dreams are fond hopes and desires that everyone thinks about. While most people dream while they're sleeping, this workbook does not focus on those types of dreams. These dreams may be about what you want to do when you're older. They may be about where you want to live and who you want to live with. They might be about wanting to go to school to study something you're interested in. Dreams involve thinking about the type of person you want to become.

Teenage years are a good time to begin thinking about hopes and dreams so you can start working towards them. Dreams can be hard to believe in if you don't think you can achieve them. Sometimes people give up on their dreams, or talk themselves out of them. It's important to know what your dreams are. When you are clear about your dreams, and let others know about them, you can often achieve them.

DREAMS

Why should I bother thinking about any hopes and dreams I have for myself?

_____

What things get in the way of following my dreams?

_____

How can I take a stand to make my dreams come true?

_____

_____

Who comes to mind when I think of someone who has struggled and made their dreams come true?

_____

_____

When am I successfully working towards any of my dreams?

_____

_____

Top 10 Dreams I Have for Myself

_____
_____
_____
_____
_____
_____
_____
_____

Courage

Courage means being able to deal with anything that's difficult. Courage is dealing with anything dangerous, difficult, or painful, instead of running away from, or ignoring it. Courage can help you make healthy choices. The more you practice courage, or dealing with hard stuff, the better life gets!

Healing pain requires courage and strength. It requires thinking about things differently than you did in the past. This workbook can help you find courage and strength to learn about health and well-being.

COURAGE

How does courage play a part in health and well-being?

_____

When am I courageous?

_____

What helps me to be courageous?

_____

_____

Who comes to mind when I think of a courageous person?

_____

_____

How do they show their courage?

_____

_____

How can I use what I know about courage to consider successful change in my life?

_____

_____

Top Things I'm Learning About Courage

_____
_____
_____
_____
_____
_____
_____
_____
_____
_____

Strength

Strength is having the power to get something done. Strength is not just about the power your muscles have to lift or move something. Strength also involves making healthy choices and sticking with them. Strength is knowing what is right and doing it. Strength is about taking a stand for something you believe in, even when you are the only one willing to do so. Strength requires hard work.

It takes great strength to become the person you want to be. Using strength to face pain can help you experience health and well-being. Strength helps you to stand tall and talk about pain honestly. When you are able to face pain, you become stronger than it is. When you are confident in having courage and strength to face pain in your life you are able to heal.

Top Things I'm Learning About Strength

_____
_____
_____
_____
_____
_____
_____
_____

STRENGTH

How does strength play a part in healing pain?

_____

What helps me to be strong?

_____

Who comes to mind when I think of a strong person?

_____

_____

How do they show their strength?

_____

_____

When do I successfully use my strength?

_____

_____

How can I use what I know about strength to consider a successful change in my life?

_____

_____

Respect

Health and well-being require respect. *Respect means showing concern for the feelings, wishes, or rights of others.* It is showing concern for yourself and for all other living things. Respect is treating everyone, and everything, with kindness and regard for well-being. When you really care for yourself and others you are able to make choices in everyone's best interest. It doesn't mean you won't feel hurt, angry, and frustrated at times. Everyone gets upset at times. It just means that when you are upset you can learn to manage pain in ways that no longer cause harm to yourself, or anyone else. You can learn to manage feelings with respect.

When children have not been treated with respect it is hard to learn how to treat others that way. It may take some practice. These questions are a place to start learning about respect and how it can help you in life.

RESPECT

How does respect play a part in health and well-being?

_____

When do I feel respected?

_____

When am I being respectful towards others?

_____

_____

Who comes to mind when I think of a respectful person?

_____

_____

How do they show respect?

_____

_____

How can I use what I know about respect to consider successful change in my life?

_____

_____

_____

Top Things I'm Learning About Respect.

_____
_____
_____
_____
_____
_____
_____
_____
_____

Conclusion

Healthy decision-making is hard work! It takes a lot of thought and practice. You can practice as you go through the workbook. Each section helps you think about yourself and your behavior so you can practice making healthy choices. This is done without causing harm to yourself or others. Life is full of temptations! Health and well-being require courage and strength to take a stand against such temptations.

It takes courage and strength to believe in yourself, especially when others may doubt you. It may also take patience with all of these questions. Daring to take a stand on behalf of yourself can be a new experience. Taking a stand for health is not for the faint-hearted. It is a very personal decision. Only you can decide what is really in your best interest.

Please take your time, and give yourself a break if it feels too hard. Taking your time helps you learn how to take good care of yourself. Relax when you need to. Your energy will most likely come back after a break. If you find you are avoiding questions because they stir up troublesome thoughts, think about how you will find the courage to tell someone you trust so they can help you along the way. You're not in this alone and there are people around you who really want to help and can help.

REFLECTIONS ON HEALTH AND WELL-BEING

When do I make successful choices?

_____

_____

Who supports these choices?

_____

_____

How interested am I in pursuing health and well-being?

_____

_____

What are some good reasons to focus on these things?

_____

_____

What gets in the way of thinking about them?

_____

_____

How ready am I to take a stand and follow my dreams?

_____

_____

How confident am I that I can do these things?

_____

_____

Chapter Two:
My Life Experiences

This workbook is about a variety of things that occur in life. The purpose of this chapter is to help you take a look at your life and think about choices you make. Looking at the different parts can help you learn more about how you act and decisions you make about health and well-being. Answering the questions is an opportunity for you to think about yourself and things that affect you. The answers can help you consider change by learning about the best ways to take good care of yourself. They can help you make decisions about becoming the person you want to be.

My Self

How you think about yourself influences how you act. When you like yourself and assume others will like you too, you are more likely to be friendly and enjoy being around others who feel the same way. If people have said bad things about you, or treated you badly, you may incorrectly think you're bad. You may also incorrectly think that all people are bad. People are very complicated! No one is either all bad or all good. Even when people have done bad things it does not mean they are all bad.

Take some time to think about yourself so you can better understand how all the different parts come together to make you who you are. How you think about yourself can be influenced by how you think others see you. Pay attention to those things you like best about yourself. Think about parts of yourself you might not be too happy with right now. Life experiences and how you see yourself influence your health and well-being. Take time to think about how you want people to see you. This will give you ideas about changes you might want to make.

MY SELF

Who and what have had the biggest effect on how I think about myself?

_____

_____

How do thoughts about myself influence health and well-being?

_____

_____

What am I learning about myself now?

_____

_____

How is this new information helping me find courage, strength and respect?

_____

_____

How can I use what I know about myself to make successful choices in my life?

_____

_____

Top Things I Like About Me

_____

_____

_____

_____

_____

_____

_____

_____

_____

Sex and Sexuality

Sexuality is everything about you that makes you who you are, not just your sexual behavior. Young people get a lot of messages about sexuality. These messages come from television, movies, the Internet, video games, families and friends, teachers and other people in your community. Unfortunately, many of these are mixed messages and do not promote sexual health. Sexual practices that do not promote sexual health can cause harm. Here are some definitions that can help you understand the challenge.

Sex refers to the categories into which most living things are divided on the basis of their reproductive functions! Whoa, what does that mean? Basically, it's the body parts, or genitals, that determine whether someone is male or female.

Sexual Health is "a state of physical, emotional, mental and social well-being in relation to sexuality; it is not merely the absence of disease, dysfunction or infirmity. Sexual health requires a positive and respectful approach to sexuality and sexual relationships, as well as the possibility of having pleasurable and safe sexual experiences, free of coercion, discrimination and violence. For sexual health to be attained and maintained, the sexual rights of all persons must be respected, protected and fulfilled" (The World Health Organization, 2007).

Sexual Harm is any sexual act that hurts someone, or any sexual act that is illegal. Sexual harm ranges from insulting remarks and sexual harassment through a variety of hands off offenses such as hazing, peeping, or exposing genitals, to specific behaviors such as sexual assault and rape. Friends, dating partners, teachers, coaches, ministers, strangers, family members, other teens, and adults can cause sexual harm. Sexual harm can occur by one, or more peers, or by one, or more adults.

Child Sexual Abuse happens when someone exploits a child for sexual stimulation. Forms of child sexual abuse include asking or pressuring a child to engage in sexual activities; showing private parts (genitals) to a child; showing pornography to a child; sexual contact against a child; touching a child's genitals; looking at a child's genitalia without touching them; or using a child to make pornography.

Coercion means using pressure, force, or threats to get someone else to do something.

Hazing is humiliating and often dangerous initiation rituals into a gang, club, or fraternity.

Sexual Harassment is unwelcome behavior of a sexual nature. It can be name-calling, sexual jokes, rumors, or gossip of a sexual nature at school or work, pestering, annoying, and stalking behavior. It does not include any physical touching.

Acquaintance, Friendship, or Date Rape is forced vaginal, oral, or anal intercourse by someone in a social relationship with a person who has not agreed to sex.

Incest is criminal sexual behavior between any family members.

Everyone expresses sexuality in unique ways. While we are all different there are categories that can help you understand differences between sexual health and sexual harm. Here is a chart to help you understand.

Sexual Health ◀ • • • • • • • • • • • • • • • • • ▶ Sexual Harm				
Healthy Age Appropriate Respectful and Safe	Mutually Flirtatious and Playful	Age Inappropriate Non Mutual	Harassment	Sexual Abuse Violence

Sexuality is a big part of everyone's life. Sexuality is a whole lot of things and it can be confusing! A person's sex usually tells us whether they are a girl or a boy, female or male, woman or man. The word sex is often used to describe the act of sexual intercourse and reproduction. *Reproduction is the process by which humans, animals and plants create new individuals.*

Sexuality is a part of everyone's life and it affects how you think and feel about yourself and others. When people confuse sex with love and affection it causes problems. Such confusion can play a huge part in sexual decision-making. It is important to clear up sexual confusion so it doesn't cause problems in your life.

Sex Roles

Some people think you are supposed to act a certain way if you are male or female. *Gender* indicates your membership in a group of males or females. *Gender messages are things you are taught to believe about what it means to be a man or woman.* Different cultures often have different gender messages. Young men hear things like "stand up and be a man". This can mean you should be honest and proud to hold your head high because of good things you have done, or should do. It might be used to try to get a young man to do something. It can also be mistaken as permission to bully others. A lot of boys think you have to be tough to be a man. Boys often get messages that you are supposed to act a certain way in order to become a "real" man. To be cool you might get pressure to hide your emotions, act fearless, and pretend to always be in control. These types of messages are called sex role, or gender messages. They are called this because they give you ideas about your "role" as a male.

Girls also get gender messages about female sex roles. Some well-known ones are "act like a lady", "be nice", and "stand by your man". Such messages can be confusing. They can also cause problems! When young women do not learn to be strong and demand respect, they can be at risk of accepting sex roles that may not be in their best interest. They may think they are supposed to accept sexual harm and/or violence in their relationships. They may not learn how to take a stand against harm in their life.

Some messages make it hard to be genuine. *Genuine means being who you really are. It is being sincere and honest and true.* Everybody has strong emotions sometimes. Everybody gets scared at times and nobody is in control all the time. Everyone should be nice!

Some messages make it easy to be genuine. Messages like "real men never hurt women" and "real women have curves" can help reduce confusion and promote health. Take some time to figure out messages you have received that influence your sexuality. See if you can make sense of them and decide what you want to do with them. You will have an opportunity to think about which ones you want to keep and which ones you want to get rid of.

GENDER MESSAGES ABOUT SEX ROLES

What gender messages did I get about both males and females?

_____

_____

How do such messages influence health and well-being?

_____

_____

What have been the biggest influences on how I think about men and women's roles?

_____

_____

What am I learning about these messages now?

_____

What challenges am I facing about sex roles?

_____

_____

How does this information help me to find courage, strength and respect?

_____

_____

How can I use what I know about these messages to make successful choices in my life?

_____

_____

Top Things I'm Learning About Sex-Roles

_____

_____

_____

_____

_____

_____

_____

_____

Sexual Arousal

Arousal is a response to a stimulus. What the heck does that mean? It simply means that your body responds to things. When you are cold (a stimulus) you want to put on warm clothing (a response). Human beings experience many types of arousal. Hunger, thirst, and physical sensations are all types of arousal. Joy, laughter, fear and anger are too.

Sexual stimulation, or arousal, is a body's physical response to something that brings on sexual feelings. Sexual arousal is one of many types of arousal. It occurs when you respond to something you find stimulating. There are a lot of things that influence sexual arousal. Exploring some of these things can help you understand how your body responds sexually to a variety of things.

Everyone experiences confusion about sexual arousal. Young people often wonder what's happening when they first experience it. If no one explains sexual arousal to a child, that child is likely to be confused when it happens, particularly the first time! Exploring your feelings about sexual arousal can help you make sense of it. Sexual arousal is different for everyone. Don't worry if you talk to others about it and you don't feel the same way they do.

Unfortunately sexual arousal can be involved in violence and sexual aggression. Since *aggression is forceful, attacking behavior*, it is hurtful. When people experience sexual harm, arousal can be hard to understand. Violence, aggression, and fear can cause sexual arousal in some people. People who have experienced sexual harm can have feelings of fear, sometimes terror, and sexual arousal all at the same time. How confusing is that! Such feelings can cause victims to blame themselves when they don't understand they couldn't control the sexual stimulation that can be a part of sexual assault. There will be more about this in another chapter. For now, it's just important to know that sexual arousal can challenging to understand.

Sexual arousal can be fun! It is something all human beings experience and it can be managed in a variety of healthy ways. Everyone feels sexually aroused at times when it is not okay to engage in sexual acts and everyone can learn how to enjoy sexual arousal without acting on it.

SEXUAL AROUSAL

How does sexual arousal play a part in health and well-being?

_____

What have been the biggest influences on my sexual arousal?

_____

What am I learning about sexual arousal now?

_____

What challenges am I facing about sexual arousal?

_____

How does this information help me find courage, strength and respect?

_____

How can I use what I know about arousal to make healthy choices?

_____

Lots of young people engage in flirtation as a way of experiencing sexual arousal and sexual pleasure. _Flirtation is playing at love_. It is showing interest in, or sexual attraction to someone. It might involve activities like good-natured joking, smiling, playing games, or dancing.

Some people confuse flirtation with teasing but they are different. _Teasing is annoying, or harassing by mocking or poking fun_. Sexual teasing can hurt people's feelings. It can be a type of sexual harassment, which is against the law.

When you find yourself becoming sexually aroused you have lots of choices about how to handle your arousal. You can ignore it until it goes away. If you are alone in a private place you may chose to masturbate. _Masturbation is stimulating your own genitals for the purpose of sexual pleasure_. If you are with a consenting partner you may engage in flirtation and other things like holding hands, hugging each other, or kissing. It is important to make sure that any of these activities are okay with your partner.

Top Ways I Can Enjoy Sexual Arousal Without Causing Harm

_____
_____
_____
_____
_____
_____
_____
_____
_____

Sexual Identity

Identity is the fact of being who a person is. Sexual identity means being who you are sexually. Some people have some confusion figuring out who they are attracted to. *Attraction means causing interest or pleasure.* People have a lot of different interests. When it comes to sexual identity most people are heterosexual. *Heterosexual means sexual attraction between people of the opposite sex. Homosexual means sexual attraction between people of the same sex.* Women who are sexually attracted to other women are lesbian, and men who are attracted to other men are gay. *People who are sexually attracted to both sexes are bi-sexual. Transgender refers to people who identify with a gender other than the one (male or female) they were born with.*

Unfortunately, some people think homosexuality is bad. Some religions say it is wrong. There is a long history of discrimination, even in American laws, towards gay, lesbian, bi-sexual and transgendered people. *Discrimination means unjust treatment.* People who are not heterosexual may be afraid to tell others about their sexual identity.

Many organizations can help young people who are confused about sexual identity. They are listed in the back of the workbook. When you want to talk with someone about your sexual identity try to find people who care about you, are trustworthy, and don't discriminate against others.

SEXUAL IDENTITY

Who am I attracted to sexually?

_____

_____

How safe do I feel expressing my sexual identity?

_____

_____

What support do I need to feel safe and secure in my sexual identity?

_____

_____

If I don't feel safe, who can provide support and understanding?

_____

_____

How can I express my sexuality in healthy ways?

_____

_____

How can I use what I know about sexual identity to protect myself from harm?

_____

_____

Sexual Pleasure

Sexual pleasure is anything a person finds to be sexually enjoyable, delightful and satisfying. Sexual pleasure involves stimulation that is not hurtful in any way.

Learning the difference between sexual arousal and sexual pleasure can help you understand yourself better. Arousal is what excites you sexually while pleasure involves intimate enjoyment of your body. *Intimate means private or personal.* People can enjoy sexual pleasure alone, or have sexual intimacy with another person who clearly agrees to share in the pleasure. It involves both giving and receiving sexual stimulation.

SEXUAL PLEASURE

How does sexual pleasure play a part in health and well-being?

_____

_____

What have been the biggest influences on how I experience sexual pleasure?

_____

_____

What am I learning about sexual pleasure now?

_____

_____

What challenges am I facing about sexual pleasure?

_____

_____

How can I use what I know about sexual pleasure to make healthy choices?

_____

_____

Sexual Intercourse

Sexual intercourse is the sexual joining of two individuals. Even though sex refers to many different things, a lot of people think of sexual intercourse whenever the topic of sex comes up. Sexual intercourse is just one way of engaging in sexual behavior. The act of sexual intercourse usually refers to a man putting his penis into a woman's vagina. Sexual intercourse can also occur between two males, or two females. Males might use their anus, or other body parts, to receive the penis, and females can use their hands, or other body parts, to sexually stimulate a partner's vagina.

The ways in which a person learns about sexual intercourse can influence thoughts, feelings and sexual behavior. Exploring these experiences can help you make sense of ways you behave sexually. It can help you make connections between your early learning and how you express your sexuality now. It can also help you to consider things you might want to change about your sexual expression.

SEXUAL INTERCOURSE

How does sexual intercourse play a part in health and well-being?

_____

What have been the biggest influences on how I think about sexual intercourse?

_____

What am I learning about sexual intercourse now?

_____

How can I use what I know about sexual intercourse to make healthy decisions?

_____

_____

What support do I need to express my sexuality without causing harm?

_____

_____

Love

Love is a deep and tender feeling of attachment. It is a very powerful emotion that influences behavior. Human beings seek love and affection naturally. *Affection is expression of fond or tender feelings*. Love is a wonderful experience when it reflects genuine care, concern and respect. Love and affection do not necessarily go together. Sometimes people feel love and do not express it through affectionate behavior. Sometimes it is hard for people to show love through tender acts of kindness and respect. They may be shy, or part of a culture that does not outwardly express love.

It is hard to believe someone loves you when they treat you badly. People who do that are not expressing love, even if they try to convince you they are. Their actions are harmful, wrong, and often criminal. Love never causes harm.

It takes courage to express love with tender affection. It takes strength to openly receive love. Love can make some people feel vulnerable. *Vulnerable means open to being wounded or easily hurt*. When children are hurt by people who are supposed to love them, they can feel vulnerable and become afraid of love. Finding the courage and strength to love with tender affection takes practice. It takes courage to face the fear of being hurt and learn that broken hearts can be mended. Strong hearts can be hurt and go on to love again. A courageous and strong heart rejects harm and protects itself through healthy choices and loving relationships.

LOVE

How does love play a part in health and well-being?

_____

_____

What have been the biggest influences on how I experience love?

_____

_____

What challenges am I facing about love?

_____

_____

How is this new information helping me find courage, strength and respect?

_____

_____

How can I use what I know about love to make a healthy choices in my life?

_____

_____

Top Things I'm Learning About Love

_____

_____

_____

_____

_____

_____

_____

_____

_____

My Family

Families play a big part in everyone's life. They greatly influence your life experiences. Where you grow up, who you grow up with, how family members act, and what your family values, all play a part in understanding yourself. Figuring out things about your family helps you learn how to handle yourself in different situations.

MY FAMILY

How has my family played a part in my health and well-being?

_____

_____

What have been the biggest influences on how I think about my family?

_____

_____

What challenges am I facing about my family?

_____

_____

How is this new information helping me find courage, strength and respect?

_____

_____

How can I use what I know about my family to make healthy choices?

_____

_____

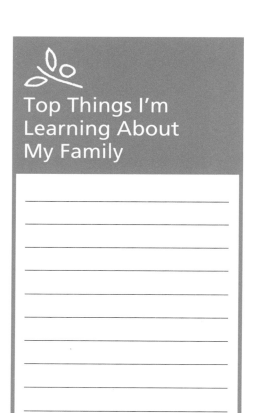

Top Things I'm Learning About My Family

_____

_____

_____

_____

_____

_____

_____

_____

_____

Education

Most young people spend a lot of time at school. Your thoughts about school play a big part in how well you do, how much you learn, and how you think about yourself. How well you learn different subjects and how you get along with others in school influences what other people, like teachers and other students, think about you. Lots of times, what others think of you influences how you think about yourself, and how you act. Because you spend so much time there, school can have a big impact on your life.

Answering questions about school can give you information about how you like to learn and what you are interested in learning. School can also give you ideas about how you like to work and what kind of work you like to do. Education can help you pursue your dreams and create new ones.

MY SCHOOL EXPERIENCES

How does school play a part in health and well-being?

_____

_____

What have been the biggest influences on how I experience school?

_____

_____

What challenges am I facing about education?

_____

_____

How is this new information helping me think about dreams I have for myself?

_____

_____

How can I use what I know about school to help me make successful choices?

_____

_____

My Community

Community is the experience of living with others. Your community consists of all the people and places you come in contact with on a regular basis. The neighborhood you live in is your immediate community. Your school is a big part of your community. If you go to a church, synagogue, mosque, or other place of worship, the other people who go there, are part of your community. Places you shop are also a part of your community. Places where you do things like getting together with friends are also a part of your community. Places where you work are a part of your community. Even the streets are a part of your community. Some people move around a lot and are influenced by a variety of communities. Communities you grow up in have a big influence on your life, whether you live in one for a long time, or a lot of different ones for different lengths of time.

MY COMMUNITY

How does my community play a part in my health and well-being?

_____

_____

What have been the biggest influences on how I experience my community?

_____

_____

What challenges am I facing in my community?

_____

_____

How does my community influence my decision-making?

_____

_____

Friendship

A friend is someone you like who provides support. Friendships occur in a variety of situations and can change over time. When you are very young friendship is mostly about playing together. As you get older, in addition to being companions, friends can provide support and help you through tough times. Friends can help you feel a deep sense of connection and belonging. Friends can influence your life. Friendships can also become painful and end due to differences of opinion, or hurtful behavior. Friends don't have to be your own age. They can be younger, or older, male or female. Friendships can grow between any people regardless of differences. Friendship is based upon care and concern for another person.

FRIENDSHIP

How does friendship play a part in health and well-being?

_____

_____

What have been the biggest influences on how I experience friendship in my life?

_____

_____

How do I pick my friends?

_____

_____

How do my friends help me practice courage, strength and respect?

_____

_____

How can I use what I know about friendship to make healthy choices in my life?

_____

_____

Conclusion

You've just finished a lot of important work about life experiences. Congratulations on a job well done! Some people go their whole life without making sense of how life experiences influence thoughts, feelings, reactions and behavior. Finding strength and courage to answer all these questions allows you to be thoughtful about what you want to do with this knowledge. Think about what you want to take control of and change so you can take good care of yourself, become the person you want to be, and pursue your dreams. Before going on you may want to review your work and reflect on your accomplishments.

REFLECTIONS ON MY LIFE EXPERIENCES

How willing am I to think about how my life experiences play a part in my health and well-being?

_____

_____

What life experiences have helped me develop skills and confidence?

_____

_____

What life experiences are hard to face?

_____

_____

How can I use courage, strength, and respect to face them?

_____

_____

How ready, willing, and able am I to take a stand for healthy decision-making?

_____

_____

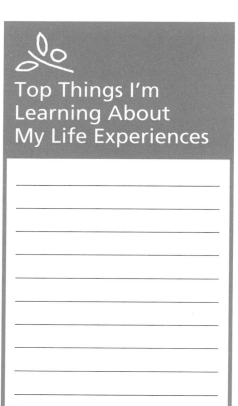

Top Things I'm Learning About My Life Experiences

_____

_____

_____

_____

_____

_____

_____

_____

_____

Chapter Three: Bad Things That Happen in Life

As children grow up, bad things sometimes happen. Bad things happen to everyone. Bad things that happened to you in the past can play a part in health and well-being. They can get in the way of taking good care of yourself and becoming the person you want to be, or they can help make you strong and successful.

In order to figure out answers you have a lot more questions. It takes a lot of questions to figure out the best ways to take good care of yourself. Many things influence sexual decision-making, so it takes some effort to figure out healthy ways to express your sexuality. Don't worry though; you can take time to answer the questions. You can answer one or two at a time, or a whole section. It doesn't matter. What matters is that you take time to think about all of this so you can figure out how to experience sexual health and well-being. Feel free to have someone you trust help you with these questions.

Some questions may be hard to answer. They bring up bad things that happened to you. It can be hard to think about those things. People seldom want to think about bad things and don't want to talk about them. It's extra hard if you tried to talk about any of these things before and nothing got better. Some young people have tried to talk about difficult things and felt it made matters worse. That's awful, and it doesn't have to be that way.

It's important to know you might feel vulnerable as you're figuring out answers to some questions. Remember, *vulnerable means easily hurt and open to criticism or attack*. Some people are afraid of feeling vulnerable. While you may be afraid of someone putting you down because of bad things that happened to you, when you're in safe company that won't happen.

You might also feel shame as you think about these things. *Shame is a painful feeling caused by bad behavior*, whether it is caused by your behavior, or the behavior of others. Some bad things that happen in life are shameful. Almost everyone has experiences that cause shame and embarrassment. *Embarrassment means feeling self-conscious or awkward*.

It's okay to be afraid to think about these things, it's okay to be nervous talking about them, and it's okay to feel shame about them. It takes courage, and strength, and people who make you feel safe, to be able to overcome this fear and shame. You can do it! Consider sharing your fears with someone you trust. It often helps people feel better. A wise woman once said that by sharing our pain it becomes less painful. She was right. But it's still scary.

When you are able to answer the questions you might be surprised by some of the feelings you have. Many people report actually feeling better after figuring out answers to these questions. Some report feeling lighter, as though a burden has been lifted off their shoulders. Others say they understand things more clearly. Once you know the answers you will be able to consider new solutions to heal pain. Healing pain without causing harm to yourself or others is the key to health and well-being.

Bad Things That Happen in Life

Sickness: When any part of your body suffers from disease or illness.

Moving: When something harmful makes you have to change the place where you live.

Loss: When someone, or something, you care about is no longer with you.

Natural Disaster: Harm caused by weather or earth related forces.

Accidents: Something unexpected that hurts people.

Poverty: Being poor and not having enough of what you need to be safe and healthy.

Prejudice: Unjust behavior towards others.

School Problems: Difficulties at school.

Social Problems: Painful or troublesome things that happen with others.

Family Problems: Trouble happening in your family.

Divorce: The ending of a marriage.

Neglect: Failure to protect and take care of children.

Verbal Abuse: Saying hurtful things that cause others to feel badly.

Emotional Abuse: Hurting people's feelings in ways that make them feel bad.

Physical Abuse: Using force to hurt others. This can be slapping, hitting, kicking, pushing, biting, pinching, or using objects to cause pain.

Sexual Abuse: Using another person sexually against their will. This includes asking or pressuring someone to engage in sexual activities against their will; showing private parts (genitals); showing pornography; unwanted sexual contact; touching genitals; looking at genitals without touching them; or using someone to make pornography.

Death: When people, or animals you care about die.

BAD THINGS THAT HAPPENED TO ME

What things have happened to me that I did not want to happen?

_____

_____

What have been the biggest influences on how I survived those things?

_____

_____

How did I keep myself going after they happened?

_____

_____

What does it say about my courage, strength, and respect?

_____

_____

What does this prove about me as a person?

_____

_____

How can I use what I know about those things to make healthy decisions?

_____

_____

How can I honor and celebrate myself for surviving?

_____

_____

How can the way I manage those things help me become the person I want to be?

_____

_____

Top Things I'm Learning About Bad Things That Happened To Me

_____

_____

_____

_____

_____

_____

_____

_____

Violence and Abuse

Violence is physical force intended to hurt, damage, or kill someone, or something. Violence happens in the media (television, in video games, movies, the Internet, and books), between people and in communities. Everyone gets a lot of messages about violence. While growing up you get the messages from parents, brothers and sisters, aunts, uncles and grandparents. You also learn about violence from friends and people outside your family. Events that happen in your neighborhood and at school teach you a lot about violence.

Thinking about violence can help you figure out what messages you've gotten about it. It can also help you consider how personal experiences with violence have influenced your health and well-being.

Some things you learn about violence may be accurate and some things you learn may not be. Sometimes it's hard to know the difference. You might not know where to get the right answers, but it's important to find them so you can learn take good care of yourself.

Taking time to identify things you have learned about violence can help you make sense of those messages. You can talk with others about how truthful the messages are. It can also help you consider changing your beliefs about violence so you can take good care of yourself.

VIOLENCE

How have I experienced violence in my life?

_____

_____

How did I survive the violence?

_____

_____

What have been the biggest influences on how I made it through those experiences?

_____

_____

What does it say about my courage, strength and respect?

_____

_____

What does this prove about me as a person?

_____

_____

How can I use what I know about violence to make healthy decisions?

_____

_____

_____
_____
_____
_____
_____
_____
_____
_____
_____

Abuse is repeated cruelty towards people or animals. Different kinds of abuse were listed with the bad things that happen in life. Verbal abuse is saying hurtful things to someone, over and over again, and causing the other person to feel badly. Physical abuse is when someone hurts another person's body, leaves marks of any kind, or causes damage inside their body. Sexual abuse occurs whenever someone uses another for his, or her, sexual needs without consent, or when the other person is too young to consent.

Emotional abuse is when someone makes you feel badly in a way that keeps you from being able to do things you should be able to do. An example of this occurs when a parent, or older person, depends on a child to take care of them and prevents the child from doing things like playing with other children, or going to school. This can happen when an adult struggles with alcohol or drug addiction. It can also happen when children are ignored and neglected. When children do not have an adult who takes good care of them they don't learn how to get their needs met.

Sometimes children are abused by people they love the most. When this happens children often feel scared, alone and lonely. It becomes hard to trust others to take care of you. You might feel it isn't safe to be in close relationships and you might have trouble connecting with others in helpful ways. You may tell yourself it's better to be alone. These are normal reactions for people abused by adults who were supposed to be taking good care of them. Me & Tobi. I screamed at him & he was shocked. I guess from then on, he lost trust & he was only 1 & 8 mths

ABUSE

How have I experienced abuse in my life?

_____

_____

How has abuse played a part in my health and well-being?

_____

_____

What have been the biggest influences on how I made it through abusive experiences?

_____

_____

How did I keep myself going after being involved in abuse?

_____

_____

What does it say about my courage, strength and respect?

_____

_____

What does this prove about me as a person?

_____

_____

How can I use what I know about abuse to make healthy choices?

_____

_____

Top Things I'm Learning About Abuse

_____

_____

_____

_____

_____

_____

_____

_____

_____

Trauma

Trauma is a very painful experience that has a lasting effect on your life. When others hurt you by saying bad things, hitting you, or touching you in sexual ways, it can hurt for a long time. The pain can be physical, emotional, or both. *Physical mean having to do with the body* and *emotional means having to do with feelings*. Emotional pain from trauma often lasts longer than any physical pain. Simple trauma is a single distressing event that causes lasting pain, while complex trauma is more than one traumatic experience that happened over time. *Complex means having many different but connected parts.* A trauma can be an injury, wound, or shocking experience. Being away from people you care about is painful and can be traumatic. Even though a lot of people go through divorce it causes a great deal of pain. Losing a family member through separation or death can be quite traumatic.

There is a difference between bad things that happen and trauma. Many bad things that happen only bother people for a short time. Some bad things may be awful when they happen, and for a while afterwards, but the pain goes away over time. You may even forget about them after a while. Pain from trauma can stick with you a long time, sometimes your whole life. Even though a lot of the pain may go away, trauma is something you never forget. Trauma can be dealt with in very healthy ways, and people can go on to lead happy lives.

TRAUMA

What traumatic things have happened to me?

_____

How has trauma played a part in my health and well-being?

_____

What have been the biggest influences on how I made it through those experiences?

_____

How did I keep myself going after those traumas?

_____

_____

What am I learning about trauma now?

_____

_____

What does this say about my courage, strength and respect?

_____

_____

What does this prove about me as a person?

_____

_____

How can I use what I know about trauma to make healthy choices?

_____

_____

All human beings need others to survive. It can be hard when you're afraid to be close to others but still want to be close to someone who treats you well. It's hard to believe they won't turn against you. The trauma of past abuse can get in the way of having good relationships in your life now. You can learn to understand abuse by talking with adults, who do not hurt you, about the information in this workbook. This can help you to learn how to take good care of yourself.

Conclusion

Whew! You've just completed a lot more hard work. Good for you! You've been getting a lot of practice being thoughtful about your life. This practice can create new ways for you to think about managing challenging experiences. This might be a good time to think back, or reflect, on what you have learned from this section.

REFLECTIONS ON BAD THINGS THAT HAPPEN IN LIFE

How hard was it to answer questions about bad things that happen in life?

_____

_____

What did it take to face up and write about those things?

_____

_____

What important things am I proving about myself?

_____

_____

What challenges am I facing about bad things that happened to me?

_____

_____

How can I use this new information to make healthy choices?

_____

_____

Chapter Four:
Looking For Love In
All The Wrong Places!

lost Policies &
Human Rights.
Educatn
Society & Cultures
Econs &
Health Systems

There's an old song called *What's Love Got To Do With It?* Love has everything to do with health and well-being! Loving, and being loved, play a big part in who we are and how we experience life. When people experience violence and abuse, love goes wrong and gets really confusing. Violence and abuse can trick people into accepting poor substitutes for love. They can make people feel unworthy of love, or believe that love involves harm. All human beings are worthy of love! And true love does not involve abuse! True love is simply based on care and concern, and does not cause harm. So what does it mean to go looking for love in all the wrong places?

Everyone has a very strong desire for love and looks for it in relationships with other living things. Families and friends are often loving, and many people love pets. People often have things they love to do, like hobbies, sports, music, art, and dance. Things we love to do often help when loving people are not around.

When children do not get enough love, and are not taught true love, they have to figure things out on their own. When people don't have good teachers, they may struggle extra hard to find the right answers. Sometimes the right answers are hard to find. When loves goes wrong confusion can prevent people from finding true love. True love is not a romantic idea like a 'soul mate' or 'special person' in your life. True love is like the golden rule of treating others the way we like to be treated. People who truly love others can accidentally hurt someone's feelings, but they apologize and make amends so there is no permanent harm. *Making amends means taking responsibility for hurting others, and making a commitment to stop it.*

Everyone feels lonely sometimes. Lonely means alone, friendless, with no one to turn to, rejected, down in the dumps, or blue. How depressing is that! Loneliness too can trick people into looking for love in all the wrong places. If someone is feeling lonely, and they don't know how to make it go away they may turn to alcohol or drugs to try to forget the pain. If they feel empty inside they may overeat in an effort to fill up the emptiness. They may have sex with someone they don't care about just to feel another human being next to them. These are all scary ways people look for love in all the wrong places. Trying to stop loneliness with alcohol and drugs can lead to addiction. Poor eating habits can lead to eating disorders and all kinds of health problems. Sex with strangers, especially when it is not protected, can put a person at risk of harm in a variety of ways. None of these activities heal pain or prevent loneliness. They actually make things worse.

When young people have been abused, lost family members, or have been removed from home, they often feel desperate to avoid loneliness. They may accept abuse in dating relationships just to have someone in their lives. They may think having a baby will cure such pain. Unfortunately healing pain doesn't work this way. Some young people mistakenly think having anyone in their life is better than being alone. They can confuse sex with love, and they can confuse parenting with love. Neither of these things cure pain and loneliness.

Young people may think love conquers all. They may think they can get an abusive partner to change just by loving them. They may think a baby can give them a perfect family, and a child who will always be with them. They may think of having a baby as a way to prove they can be a better parent than their parents were. These are not ways to find true love.

True loves comes from knowing that life isn't perfect, and people are not perfect. It comes from understanding that true love begins when you learn to love yourself by taking good care of yourself. It comes from taking a stand against violence and abuse by sharing love with others who treat you with respect and care. It comes from understanding that having children is a big responsibility requiring education and maturity so a child is not born into poverty where they are likely to stay when their parents are young people.

Learning to manage loneliness can actually be fun! Figuring out things we love to do can greatly improve health and well-being. Doing enjoyable things can make loneliness go away. Having fun can bring great joy to life! It can help people heal pain and get on with life.

LOOKING FOR LOVE

How have I been looking for love in my life?

_____

_____

What am I learning about my need for love now?

_____

_____

What does this say about my courage, strength and respect?

_____

_____

What does this prove about me as a person?

_____

_____

How can I use what I know about looking for love to make healthy choices?

_____

_____

What are some things I enjoy doing that may help reduce loneliness in my life?

_____

_____

Power and control and connection are basic needs that influence a lot of human behavior. Everyone wants something in life and everyone has a desire to manage, or direct, how things happen. All human beings must connect with others in order to stay alive. These things are all related to feeling good about yourself. Learning about them can help you understand how they influence healthy choices.

Some people say violence and abuse are about power and control. Abusive use of power and control play a part in decisions to commit acts of violence and sexual aggression. They are not the only things that influence harmful behavior.

The ways you learn to connect with others play a big part in health and well-being. When children are treated respectfully with care and concern they learn to treat others the same way. When children do not receive love in a way that helps them grow and do well, connecting with others can be confusing and scary. Such confusion and fear may influence a child to behave in harmful ways.

Secrecy is a way to hide harmful behavior. When life's pain feels unmanageable some people get confused and try to cover up the pain with anger. Desperate and confused needs for power, control and connection, mixed up with secrecy, can influence anger that results in all kinds of harm.

This section of the workbook addresses how abusive use of power, control and connection feed on secrecy and anger to influence harm. It also addresses ways you can consider using power and control in helpful ways. When you are able to do this, connection with others is respectful and caring. Letting go of destructive secrets helps people honestly face needs for power, control and connection in ways that no longer cause harm. This work is a big part of health and well-being!

Connection

Connection is like attachment, which means to come together through respect and care. Connection is how people relate to others. It relates to family ties and how people act towards those closest to them. Connection means joining together with.

How parents behave towards children impacts how children relate to others. When children receive love and affection, and are well cared for, it is easy to feel close to others and to trust that good things can happen in life. When children do not receive this type of care it is hard to learn how to connect with others. All human beings need connection through human touch in order to stay alive. When people need human connection they reach out to touch and to be touched. Their needs are met when they connect with others through affection. This might be a handshake, or a pat on the back. If it is someone they are close to it might be a hug and/or a kiss.

Tobi — felt neglected was neglected out of ignorance, but what does it matter, he was neglected, that's what counts!

When children have not had supportive attachments they cannot trust that touch will be affectionate. They may be afraid to connect with others. However, since everyone needs to be touched, they may try to connect with others in harmful ways. If a child feels desperate to be touched he, or she, may lash out in violent, or sexually aggressive ways, just to touch someone else. If they have been touched in harmful ways, they might think it's okay to touch others the same way. Such behavior is dangerous and causes a lot of problems.

Even if you had experiences like this, you can learn to connect with others in wonderful ways. You have opportunities every day to connect with others through respectful care and affection. You can learn to touch others in ways that make them feel good, and make you feel great! It may take practice but it's worth it.

Top Things I'm Learning About Connection

_____
_____
_____
_____
_____
_____
_____
_____
_____

Top 10 Benefits of Connection and Touch

1. Affection
2. Relaxation
3. Reduce loneliness
4. Enjoyment
5. Giving love
6. Soothing
7. Calming
8. Caring
9. Healing
10. Receiving love

CONNECTION

How do the ways I experience connection in my life play a part in my health and well-being?

_____

What have been the biggest influences on how I experience connection with others?

_____

What challenges am I facing about the ways I connect with others?

_____

How can I use what I know about connection to make healthy choices?

_____

Power

The word power has a lot of meanings. *It is an ability to do something, to exert force or energy*. It is when a person has influence or authority to rule, govern or dominate. Power can also be strength. Power is not good or bad, it's just power. Everyone has a desire for power, and everyone wants to be able to do something, no matter how simple it may be. Everyone has some power. The power to keep shoes on your feet comes from learning to tie shoelaces so shoes don't fall off. Most people have power to attract attention through words and actions. A desire to influence others makes people want to be powerful. Power can influence how we think about ourselves, and how others think about us.

Power is used in a lot of different ways. Many people use power to do good things and to make our world a better place to live. Some people have personal power that comes from being strong, courageous, smart, kind, and good. Other people have power that comes from a position they are in such as parents, bosses, politicians, teachers, or ministers. Some people have both personal and positional power. Benevolent power is used to make things better and to benefit people. *Benevolent means kind and good.* Many powerful people use education to obtain things that are important to them.

The President of the United States is often considered the most powerful man in the world. His power is both personal and positional. His personal power comes from having a personality people like and want to vote for. It also comes from his beliefs about what he thinks is best for the country. This is why people vote for him. His positional power comes from getting elected to be President. Getting elected took education, money, and connections with other powerful people. Once he's elected, the President uses his power in a lot of different ways. Everyone hopes the President uses power benevolently.

Jasmine was only 10 years old when she was involved with the court for sexually harming other children her age. She thought the behavior was okay because other kids had done the same things to her. Her mom couldn't protect her so the court sent Jasmine to live with her grandparents. In their home she learned healthy ways to get attention and to get her needs met. She started doing well socially and in school. Living in a stable environment and getting the right type of therapy helped Jasmine find the courage and power to tell the rest of her story. She felt safe enough to share that her mother had been sexually abusing her for years. Making sense of her past trauma and settling into her new life with her grandparents helped Jasmine to be the respectful person she always wanted to be. She began doing typical child activities, keeping herself and those around her safe, and planning for a successful future. Jasmine learned to end abusive power in her life by putting a stop to sexual harm, both hers, and her mother's.

Sometimes people use power to hurt others. This is called abusive power. It can happen when someone feels powerless to manage confusion about painful experiences. It can happen when a person learns to be mean and is taught to hurt others. Wherever it comes from, it is a way people use force to cause harm.

Making sense of power can help you understand how you, and others use it. It can also help you practice using it in good ways. Many people believe that benevolence is the highest form of power. If you really want to be powerful consider all of the ways you can use it to gain influence. You can use your personal power to take good care of yourself. You can use it to do good things. Using power in this way influences others to look up to you as an admirable person. *Admirable means deserving respect and approval.* Good things come to people who use power benevolently.

POWER

How is power playing a part in my health and well-being?

_____

_____

What have been the biggest influences on how I experience power?

_____

_____

Who comes to mind when I think of someone who uses power benevolently?

_____

_____

What challenges am I facing about power?

_____

_____

How can I use what I know about power to make healthy choices?

_____

_____

Top Ways I Can Use Benevolent Power

_____

_____

_____

_____

_____

_____

_____

_____

Control

Control means to exercise authority over, to direct, or command. Just like power, control is not good or bad, it's just control. Everybody wants to have some control in life. Control can be as basic as adjusting a thermostat so that the air in a room is warmer or cooler. Control gets more complicated when it comes to learning how to drive a car or controlling behavior. It can be very confusing when it feels like things are out of control and you don't know how to get control. Learning to control your thoughts, feelings, and behavior can help you feel powerful. It can help you make decisions about health and well-being, and it can help you take good care of yourself.

Harmful acts can look like out-of-control behavior, but they're not. They occur when people think they have no other way to manage, or control, a difficult situation. People have a lot of other ways to experience control. You can gain greater control of your life by educating yourself about things that are important to you. The knowledge you are gaining here can help when you feel like life is out of control. You can figure out what you want to have greater control of so that you can heal pain. Taking control of your life means becoming the person you want to be and pursuing your dreams.

CONTROL

When has my life felt out of control?

When do I feel out of control?

What challenges am I facing about control?

How can gaining control of my life help me use courage, strength and respect?

How can I use what I know about control to make healthy choices?

Top Things I'm Learning About Control

Secrecy

Keeping harmful things secret is very dangerous. Secrecy means to hide something. When it comes to looking for love in all the wrong places, secrets are poison! Violence and abuse depend a lot on secrecy in order to maintain the threat of abusive power and control. When people find courage and strength to report harm, secrets lose their power and can be brought to the attention of people who can help.

Secrets confuse the difference between telling and 'tattling'. *Telling is reporting information to get help.* Tattling is telling on someone in order to get him or her in trouble. It can be easier to break the spell of secrecy when you know that telling the truth can help someone, often yourself.

There are differences between secrecy, privacy, confidentiality, and surprises. While privacy and confidentiality protect personal information and relationships, secrecy is about hiding these things. Surprises are a fun part of life. Keeping something secret for a surprise is totally different than secrets about harm.

SECRECY

What have been the biggest influences on how I experience secrecy?

_____

_____

What am I learning about secrecy now?

_____

_____

What challenges am I facing about keeping secrets?

_____

_____

How is this new information helping me find courage, strength and respect?

_____

_____

How can I use what I know about secrecy to make healthy choices?

_____

_____

Top Ways To Get Rid Of Secrets

_____
_____
_____
_____
_____
_____
_____
_____
_____

Anger

Anger is a strong feeling of being upset. It comes from cruelty and often causes a desire to fight back. *Cruelty is behavior that causes pain and suffering.* When bad things happen, people often feel fear and powerlessness. It may feel like things are out of control. When people feel powerless, and out of control, they may want to get away from such feelings. This is where anger comes into the picture.

Anger can be powerful motivation to right a wrong, and it can be used benevolently. But anger can fool you if it influences you to lash out against injustice. When anger causes harm, it brings more pain and suffering. It does not solve problems, or take away pain. It's can be hard to control angry feelings, but letting them get out of control adds to problems, and makes things worse.

Young people who look for love in all the wrong places may be struggling with anger they haven't found a way to control. They may not have found a way to heal and forgive people who hurt them. Like, Jasmine, disrespecting others sexually may be a mixed up way of coping with pain. Lashing out at others may be a way of trying to punish those who caused pain and trauma. When people don't know how to manage pain they might try to disguise it as anger. But it's still pain. Anger can be a desperate attempt to cover up pain that feels unmanageable.

Attending to pain prevents anger from turning into harmful behavior. Learning to face pain means you can heal it rather than create more problems. *Resentment, which is feeling bitter about being treated unfairly,* doesn't build up when you work to heal pain. Facing pain, and healing prevents people from getting stuck, and not being able to move forward.

ANGER

How does anger play a part in health and well-being?

_____

_____

What have been the biggest influences on how I deal with anger?

_____

_____

What am I learning about anger now?

_____

_____

What challenges am I facing about ways I manage anger?

_____

_____

How is this new information helping me use power and control benevolently?

_____

_____

How can I use what I know about anger to make healthy choices?

_____

_____

Top Ways I can Express Anger Respectfully

_____

_____

_____

_____

_____

_____

_____

_____

_____

Conclusion

You've just spent a lot of time learning how people go looking for love in all the wrong places. Many people take a lot longer to figure these things out, and some people never do. By making sense of how you want to experience power, control, and connection in your life you are able to really consider how you want to take good care of yourself. When you make healthy decisions you are daring to take a stand for yourself and your well-being. When you courageously accept pain without turning it into anger you become stronger and learn to bear pain without allowing it to cause more problems. You can do this!

Human connection is very powerful! A quest for power and control alone can fool people into thinking those things are most important, but that's not true. Many boys are told that intimacy and close loving relationships are not important, or are a sign of weakness. This is not true either! Girls may believe they are supposed to accept abusive power and control from dating partners. Forget that!

Genuine strength comes from knowing you have power to gain control of your life in ways that make you feel good. Learning that you have value and are worthwhile comes from supportive and loving relations. When you know this about yourself you are able to consider what kind of caring

relationships you want to have with yourself and anyone you choose.

REFLECTION ON LOOKING FOR LOVE IN ALL THE WRONG PLACES

How has it been helpful to answer questions about looking for
love in all the wrong places?

_____

_____

How is it helping me to think differently about myself?

_____

_____

What does this prove about me as a person?

_____

_____

How can this information help me take good care of myself and
become the person I want to be?

_____

_____

Chapter Five: The Trauma Outcome Process

Top 10 Benefits of Healing

1. Feeling less pain
2. Finding truth
3. Enjoying life
4. Practicing benevolence
5. Exploring well-being
6. Behaving with honor
7. Feeling good about yourself
8. Considering intimacy
9. Giving and receiving love
10. Forgiveness

The Trauma Outcome Process is a way of understanding how past trauma affects current choices and behavior. It can help heal pain by using thoughts, feelings, reactions, and behavior to prevent harm. Healing provides a way to pursue dreams and become the person you want to be.

Healing

To heal means to make well. It is part of the word healthy. Everyone can heal pain by learning how to manage trauma without causing harm. When you practice making healthy choices you might be surprised at how much better you feel. You might feel more powerful and in control of your life. You might also be surprised to learn you can control most of the trouble in your life. You can learn how to protect yourself and others from harm. You can be close to others and learn to touch, and be touched, in ways that make you feel great!

This section focuses on healing pain in your life so you can become the person you want to be and pursue your dreams. Remember, benevolence is a desire to do good. It is kind and charitable action. Healing occurs through benevolence. Benevolence can be directed towards yourself and others. When you accept kindness and care from people who genuinely want to help you are taking a stand for healing. Like respect, benevolence is both given and received. It takes practice to be good at both giving and receiving.

The trauma outcome process is a tool to help people heal painful life experiences. Some parts of it can be confusing so plan to talk about it with people you trust. Pace yourself, and take it easy. Working through this information is an important step in healing. It is a way to practice benevolence since you are being kind to yourself when you give yourself time to think things through.

Confusion

There are a lot of reasons to consider health and well-being. It's easy to get confused about painful things in life. Sometimes confusion influences people to cause harm. Everyone's response to pain is a result, or outcome, of life experiences.

Figuring out confusion can help you heal pain. You can't prevent all pain in your life, but you can stop causing unnecessary pain. Unnecessary means not needed. You can do this by figuring out what causes pain. Then you can figure out how to protect yourself, and others, from it.

Action you can take to ease confusion is called a process. This is why the workbook is called *T.O.P*. *T.O.P.* stands for *Trauma Outcome Process*. The workbook gives you ways to stop causing harm to yourself, and others, by practicing healthy ways to manage pain from trauma.

T.J. experienced a lot of confusing things in life. He was in foster care for over a year when he was an infant because his mother drank too much alcohol and neglected him. He hadn't seen his father since he was five years old and he didn't know why. In a meeting with a counselor his mother said he was sexually abused while visiting his father, but he didn't remember it. His parents had so many partners when he started school he didn't know what his last name was. He was confused because he thought it was different than what the teacher said it was. He remembered being beaten with switches by his father's ex-wife and he recalled trying to burn up one of his mother's boyfriends who treated him badly. T.J thought his mother loved her other children more than him. He was hurt and confused by all of these things and he got into criminal trouble.

Top 10 Confusing Things In My Life

_____

_____

_____

_____

_____

_____

_____

_____

_____

_____

The Trauma
Outcome Process

Trauma

Trauma
Cues

Sight
Sound
Smell
Taste
Touch

Trauma
Echoes

Thoughts
Feelings
Bodily Reactions
Behavior
Bad Memories
Nightmares or Night Terrors
Flashbacks

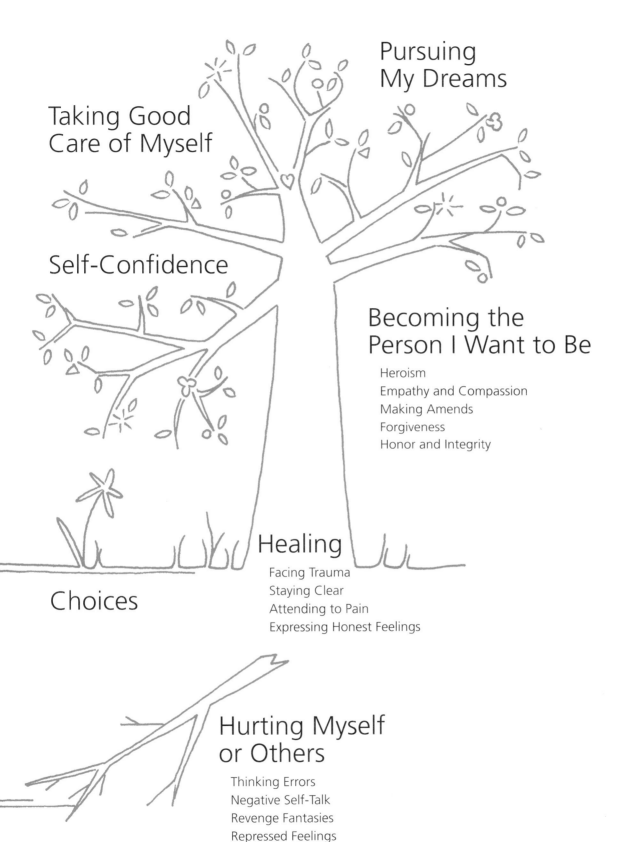

Pursuing
My Dreams

Taking Good
Care of Myself

Self-Confidence

Becoming the
Person I Want to Be

Heroism
Empathy and Compassion
Making Amends
Forgiveness
Honor and Integrity

Healing

Facing Trauma
Staying Clear
Attending to Pain
Expressing Honest Feelings

Choices

Hurting Myself
or Others

Thinking Errors
Negative Self-Talk
Revenge Fantasies
Repressed Feelings
Harmful and Offending Behavior

Facing Trauma

Facing bad things in life is a step towards healing pain caused by those things. When you are able to face them it may hurt, but at least you are clear about what's causing the pain. Once you know where pain is coming from you can figure out what you can do to stop it. It's kind of like going to the doctor. A doctor figures out where pain is coming from so you can get the right treatment. Instead of feeling like pain makes you lose control, you can learn to control it. When you learn to control pain, in ways that don't cause harm, you begin to heal.

Taking good care of yourself means facing bad things that happened to you. You began in the last section and there's more to do now. Please take some more time to think about those things and add any things you forgot so you can make sense of them. It can still be scary so you might want to have someone you trust around to help. People you trust can help you feel safe while finding courage and strength to face the pain. Sometimes pain caused by trauma comes up in unexpected ways and takes you by surprise. These situations can be scary, confusing, and really hard to manage. It might be hard but you can learn to figure them out so it's not so painful.

Trauma Cues

Most people have five senses. They are sight, sound, touch, smell, and taste. These senses tell your brain what's going on around you. People generally manage pain from trauma pretty well and don't think about it all the time. Then, all of a sudden, painful feelings come up that remind you of bad things that happened. These are called trauma cues. *A trauma cue is signal from one, or more of your senses that sets off a response to past trauma.* An example of this is when you see someone who reminds you of somebody who hurt you. Your sense of sight is cueing your brain to remember pain the other person caused

Kevin decided to tell his mom about some bad things she didn't know about that happened to him when he was little. After he told her he felt very anxious and nervous. That evening he tried to pick a fight with another boy. The next morning he was still upset and started crying in the cafeteria at school. He didn't want anyone to see him crying so he got up and ran out. He ran into two teachers and began hitting them. They had to hold him down for twenty minutes before he was able to get up and go to the office.

Kevin later figured out that talking about the bad things cued him back to a time when he had been abused. He felt helpless, powerless and out of control. When he was little he didn't think his connection with his mom was safe enough to tell her about it. For ten years Kevin reacted to trauma cues that brought up old feelings and caused a lot of unnecessary pain. Kevin got into therapy and was able to learn how to face the pain without causing any harm.

you. It then influences you to act in response to the bad feelings it brings up. In the past trauma cues like that may have caused you to act in harmful ways. It doesn't have to be that way.

Here's an activity to help you begin making sense of your trauma outcome process.

TRAUMA CUES

How do any of the five senses remind me of trauma in my life?

Things, or people I:

See: _____

Smell: _____

Taste: _____

Touch: _____

Hear: _____

When do I successfully manage trauma cues without causing harm?

_____

How can I use this new information to make healthy choices?

_____

_____

Once you begin to identify trauma cues you can learn to think more about them and slow down your reactions. *A reaction is a feeling, or action in response to something. It is an action brought on by resistance to another action.* When people react to trauma cues they are at risk of behaving in ways that cause more trouble. You can learn to identify trauma cues, think about them, pay attention to feelings they bring up, and your body's reaction in order to plan a healthy response. *A healthy response is a thoughtful answer that does not cause harm.* You can learn to respond to trauma cues in ways that do not cause harm to yourself or others. You can learn to respond rather than react.

Top Things I'm Learning About Trauma Cues

_____

_____

_____

_____

_____

_____

_____

_____

_____

Trauma Echoes

Trauma cues lead to trauma echoes. *An echo is a repetition of something else. In this case it is thoughts, feelings and bodily reactions that imitate past trauma and keep coming back, or repeating parts of it.* Sometimes trauma echoes can make it seem like the trauma is happening all over again, right now.

Trauma echoes affect your feelings, thoughts, bodily reactions, and behaviors. The human body reacts very quickly to trauma cues and can cause trauma echoes to come on with lightening speed. You may become tense and feel your body tighten up. You may clench your fists, or feel your blood heat up your neck and face. You may catch your breath or have trouble breathing. You might feel like you want to run away as fast as you can, or you may feel like you want to fight. You may freeze, feel overwhelmed, or shut down altogether. When your body does these things, thoughts can be racing really fast in you head. You may feel confused and struggle to figure out what's going on in your brain. You might feel powerless to do anything about it. You may believe the trauma is actually happening again. This is called a 'flashback'. Trauma echoes can also be bad memories, bad dreams, nightmares, or night terrors. When you experience trauma echoes you might think you're out of control, but you're not.

Mary realized she was reacting to trauma echoes when she was having unprotected sex with anyone who asked. She told an adult she trusted that she didn't like sleeping around all that much and she dared to take a stand to only have sex when she felt like it, with someone she liked, and she began using protection at all times. She decided to start talking to trusted adults about things that were bothering her instead of looking for love in all the wrong places. She got the courage to say no, and learned to protect herself by paying attention to what she really wanted for herself.

TRAUMA ECHOES

What types of trauma echoes have I had?

_____

_____

Flashbacks...

_____

_____

Bad dreams, or nightmares, about...

_____

_____

Painful memories include...

_____

_____

I struggle at night with terror about...

_____

_____

When do I successfully manage trauma echoes without causing any harm?

_____

_____

How can I use this new information to make healthy choices?

_____

_____

Top Things I'm Learning About Trauma Echoes

_____

_____

_____

_____

_____

_____

_____

_____

_____

Choices

The good news is you have lots of choices. Yes, choices! It might not seem like it, but you do. Even when things are happening so fast you can make choices about how to respond. When trauma echoes were influencing harm you may not have realized you had choices about how to respond. If you felt powerless, and out of control, you may have tried to gain control of a difficult situation by using power in harmful ways.

Finding courage and strength to make healthy choices is the most important part of healing and learning to take good care of yourself. I'll bet there have been times you were struggling and you made healthy choices to stay out of trouble. Think about those times. Remembering successful choices can help you plan to be even more successful! It's like those home runs that were mentioned earlier in the workbook.

In the past, when you hurt yourself, or others, you made choices to do so. You reacted harmfully instead of slowing down your thoughts and feelings in order to respond in healthy ways. You have the power to do things differently. You can control your actions and stop causing pain.

CHOICES

What choices have I been making that end up causing me harm?

_____

_____

How have I been causing harm to others?

_____

_____

When have I responded to a trauma echo and made healthy choices?

_____

_____

What does this prove about my courage, strength, and respect?

_____

_____

How am I choosing to heal from my own trauma?

_____

_____

How ready, willing and able am I to take a stand for health and well-being?

_____

_____

Top Things I'm Learning About Making Healthy Choices

_____
_____
_____
_____
_____
_____
_____
_____
_____
_____

Thinking Errors

You may have received some incorrect messages about violence and abuse. Such message may have influenced you to think in ways that are not correct. These are called 'thinking errors'. Trauma can cause people to create, and believe, thinking errors. If you were abused you may think everyone abuses others. This is a thinking error. Most people go through life and never abuse others. If you were treated badly by adults you may think all adults hurt children. This is a thinking error. Most adults treat children with love and care. If someone you loved got sick and died, you may think anyone you love will leave you. This is a thinking error. Most people have loving relationships throughout their lives. If you don't get to see your dad, you may think all dads don't care about their children. This is a thinking error. Most fathers care deeply about their children. If you have unprotected sex, you may think getting pregnant, or getting a disease will never happen to you. This is a thinking error. People get pregnant and diseased from unprotected sex. When you've had bad things happen, it makes sense that you might have thinking errors. But they're still not true.

Revenge Fantasies

When you have trauma echoes, thinking errors can get in the way of healthy choices. When you believe a thinking error, it causes problems. If you believe all people hurt others, and trauma echoes bring up thoughts and feelings about someone who hurt you, you might think something like "I better get them before they get me." This kind of thinking can only get you in more trouble. When you create fantasies to hurt others you're in danger of causing more pain. *Fantasies are unfulfilled desires. They are thoughts about doing something you think you might like to do but normally would not do.* Fantasies are not necessarily good or bad, they're just fantasies. Fantasies can often be wonderful ways to imagine better things. Revenge fantasies are a desire to get back at someone and hurt them. Most people fantasize about getting back at others who have cause them harm. As long as they remain fantasies, they may not cause more trouble.

Revenge fantasies can be dangerous and lead to more harm. If you think revenge can heal pain, you're wrong! Revenge fantasies can fool you into thinking that hurting others is okay. Revenge only makes things worse.

Take some time to think about how your thoughts and feelings affect your actions. How does your thinking influence ways you manage trauma echoes? The more you know about thinking errors and revenge fantasies the more you're able to expect and prepare for them. This allows you to make a plan for practicing healthy decision-making.

THINKING ERRORS AND REVENGE FANTASIES

What makes me want to get revenge?

_____

_____

What thinking errors and revenge fantasies have caused me problems in the past?

_____

_____

When am I successful in managing thinking errors and revenge fantasies?

_____

_____

How can I use what I know about thinking errors and revenge fantasies to make healthy choices?

_____

_____

Top Things I'm Learning About Thinking Errors and Revenge Fantasies

_____

_____

_____

_____

_____

_____

_____

_____

Hurting Others

People can cause harm in a variety of ways. Harmful behavior includes things like saying bad things to, or about, someone; being rude and disrespectful; and destroying things. These are things that hurt relationships but don't get people in trouble with the law. Such behavior gets you in trouble with other people. Harm gets in the way of respectful connection with others.

Offending Acts

Offending acts are criminal acts that get people in trouble with the law. Laws define specific offenses people can be arrested for. People who chose to hurt others through their trauma outcome process may commit both harmful and offending acts.

HARMFUL AND OFFENDING BEHAVIOR

How did I learn about hurting others?

_____

_____

When have I behaved in harmful or offending ways?

_____

_____

Who has been hurt by my harmful behavior?

_____

_____

What damage have I caused?

_____

_____

When do I choose not to cause harm?

_____

_____

What does this prove about my courage, strength and respect?

_____

_____

How does it show I can use power, control and connection in benevolent ways?

_____

_____

What does it say about my efforts to heal pain?

_____

_____

How can I use what I know about causing harm to make healthy choices?

_____

_____

Top Things I'm Learning About Harmful and Offending Behavior

_____

_____

_____

_____

_____

_____

_____

_____

Thinking Errors About Hurting Myself

Some thinking errors lead people to believe that bad things that happened were their fault, even when they weren't. Bad things can happen through no fault of your own. Some bad things that happen may be your fault. Sometimes bad things just happen and they're nobody's fault. If you were abused in any way it was not your fault. No matter how badly you might behave no one has a right to abuse you. Abuse is against the law. If you think you are to blame for things that were not your fault this is a burden you don't need, or deserve.

People create thinking errors when they do not have clear information about things that happen. If people who hurt you said things like "you're no good" or "it's all your fault", you might believe them. Those things are not true! You may have done bad things but that doesn't mean you are bad. It just means you've done some bad things.

Many children whose parents get divorced blame themselves for breaking up their parents marriage. That's a thinking error. Adults get divorced when they don't want to be together any more. Divorce seldom has anything to do with children. Take some time to explore thinking errors you may be struggling with.

Top 10 Thinking Errors About Hurting Myself

1. I'm bad
2. It's all my fault
3. I'm stupid
4. I can't do anything right
5. Nobody could ever like me
6. I'm untrustworthy
7. I'm worthless
8. Nothing matters
9. Nobody cares
10. Nothing is ever going to change

Michael had a thinking error that "tears are bad." He went to great lengths to avoid crying. He began telling himself that "when I cry I want to hit something". He would often hit walls with his hands or bang his head against a wall to try to manage pain without crying. It didn't work, and at first Michael didn't realize that hurting his hands and head were just adding problems instead of solving them. Michael learned to accept tears as a normal response to pain. He realized there are times when he needs to cry about the pain in his life. He prefers to do so privately but he knows that tears are an important part of healing.

Negative Self-Talk

Everyone has a voice inside his or her head. This voice is often how we think. It is the voice of things we say to ourselves all the time. Thinking errors about causing bad things, or blaming yourself for things that were not your fault, can lead you to tell yourself bad things. Negative self-talk can influence hurting yourself. This can be very dangerous.

There's a song by the Goo Goo Dolls called *Iris*. A line in the lyrics says 'you bleed just to know you're alive'. Some young people are at risk of causing self-harm if they believe such a statement. If the voices inside their heads repeat such words over and over, they may do something harmful to see if it's true.

THINKING ERRORS AND NEGATIVE SELF-TALK

What makes me want to hurt myself?

_____

_____

What thinking errors and negative self-talk have caused me problems in the past?

_____

_____

When do I control thinking errors and negative self-talk to prevent harm to myself?

_____

_____

What does this prove about my courage, strength and respect for myself?

_____

_____

How is this new information helping me to use power, control and connection in helpful ways?

_____

_____

How can I use what I know about thinking errors and negative self-talk to make healthy choices?

_____

_____

Top Things I'm Learning About Controlling Negative Self-Talk
_____
_____
_____
_____
_____
_____
_____
_____
_____

Repressed Feelings

To repress means to keep down or hold back. Repress also means to control so strictly as to prevent natural expression. Repressed feelings are those feelings you want to run away from, or bury somewhere deep inside. You may try to push bad thoughts and feelings away so you don't have to think about them, or feel them. That takes a lot of energy! It's like trying to run away from yourself. You can't do it! When people try to run away from trauma echoes, or push aside, things get worse. Bad thoughts just keep coming and the more people try to get rid of them the more they just keep coming back. It's exhausting! When this happens you don't have energy to talk to people, you don't have energy to feel anything, and you don't have energy to heal pain. These things can influence depression and harm to self.

After a while you may feel numb. Numb is being deprived of feelings or movement. It's almost impossible to take good care of yourself when you're numb. Numbness prevents you from being aware of what is happening to you and how things are impacting you.

Taking time to think about how you've tried to repress feelings can help you figure out how trauma can influence harm to self. When you know what you have been trying to push aside, or run away from, you can face it head on. You can use your strength and courage to manage pain. You can dare to take a stand for your health and well-being.

Be careful answering these questions, as you might feel vulnerable for a while. You might feel confused and impatient. You might also feel scared, so make sure you're safe. You might want to have someone you trust close by. When you are willing to face pain you may worry that you won't know what to do with it. You might begin to have strong feelings that come with pain. Some of those feelings might be sadness, terror, loneliness, and isolation. When you accept feelings of pain and grief about trauma healing is occurring. The intensity of pain can be terrifying. Facing that pain is an important way that healing truly occurs. When you have courage to face the pain you realize you are able to get through it and come out on the other side. This is healing. You can do it.

REPRESSED FEELINGS

What bad things caused me to try to turn off, or repress feelings?

_____

_____

What thoughts and feelings scare me?

_____

_____

When do I successfully face pain?

_____

_____

What does this prove about my courage and strength?

_____

_____

How is this new information helping me to use power, control and connection in helpful ways?

_____

_____

How can I use what I know about repressed feelings to make healthy choices?

_____

_____

Top Things I'm Learning About Accepting Feelings

_____

_____

_____

_____

_____

_____

_____

_____

_____

Hurting Myself

When you don't know how, or don't have energy to take good care of yourself, trauma echoes can influence harm to self. People who haven't found the strength and courage to make sense of their trauma outcome process are often confused about how to manage pain. Since thoughts and feelings get so mixed up it's not surprising that self-harm can be part of that confusion. People can react to trauma echoes by hurting themselves in a variety of ways.

Some acts of self-harm are easy to identify like smoking; drinking alcohol, or taking drugs; making dangerous sexual decisions; and attempting suicide. Some self-harm is hard to figure out. It is harmful to hang out in dangerous places; remain in abusive relationships; drive recklessly; hit walls; or pick fights. You can hurt yourself by eating too much or too little. Scratching or rubbing your body until you bleed or cause a sore is self-mutilation. *Mutilation means to damage or injure.* Mutilation is very dangerous! You don't have to do those things. Self-harm is a destructive way of trying to avoid painful thoughts, feelings, and reactions. Self-harm never heals pain! It creates more pain! You can find ways to stop hurting yourself.

HURTING MY SELF

What harmful things have I done to myself?

_____

_____

When was I likely to do those things?

_____

_____

What damage has my self-harm caused?

_____

_____

When do I choose not to hurt myself?

_____

_____

What does this new information prove about my courage, strength and respect for myself?

_____

_____

How can I use what I know about self-harm to make healthy choices?

_____

_____

Top Things I'm Learning to Stop Self-Harm

_____

_____

_____

_____

_____

_____

_____

_____

_____

Conclusion

Once again it's time to give yourself credit for all the hard work you've been doing! I hope you are getting a lot of good feedback about your efforts. This is extremely important work and you deserve a lot of credit! I recommend you take some time to let all of this information sink in.

In this section you focused a great deal on making sense of how bad things that happened to you come back through the trauma outcome process. That process may have influenced you to make harmful choices. Everyone faces this same challenge because everyone has bad things happen at some point in life. It takes constant practice to manage your trauma outcome process in ways that do not cause harm. This is how you heal pain.

REFLECTIONS ON THE TRAUMA OUTCOME PROCESS

How is learning about the trauma outcome process helpful?

_____

_____

What has it taught me about myself?

_____

_____

What did it take to face up to my trauma outcome process?

_____

_____

What am I proving about myself as a person?

_____

_____

What challenges am I facing about my trauma outcome process?

_____

_____

Who do I want to share the trauma outcome process with to help them heal pain in their lives?

_____

_____

Chapter Six:
Taking Good Care
of yourself

You are already practicing taking good care of yourself by answering questions in this workbook. When it comes to health and well-being, the trauma outcome process gives you a way to better understand thoughts, feelings, bodily reactions, and behavior relating to bad things that happened in your life. This section can help you to create a plan for practicing healthy decision-making.

Facing Trauma

The first task is to recognize trauma. You have been doing this since completing the section about bad things that happen in life. You may think of other things you forgot and can add them to your answers. There may be others things that have happened since you filled out those answers. The more courage you have to face trauma, and attend to pain it causes, the more able you are to take good care of yourself. Letting people you trust know about pain in your life is not a weakness. It is actually an act of courage and strength. Truly strong people are able to acknowledge pain without allowing it to cause more pain. Daring to share your pain and resolve it will not get the best of you! Doing those things are acts of benevolent power and control. It is proof that you can use the power of words and respectful connection to make healthy choices. So every time you face painful events you are taking responsibility for healing.

Top 10 Important Things About Facing Trauma In Healthy Ways

1. Slow down!
2. Find courage to think about it
3. Tell someone you trust
4. Write about it
5. Bring it up in therapy
6. Express it through drawing or music
7. Meditate, or pray about it
8. Read workbooks about healing
9. Watch shows about healing
10. Be patient with yourself and others

FACING TRAUMA

How does facing trauma without causing harm play a part in taking good care of myself?

_____

Are there traumatic experiences I have not talked with anyone about?

_____

_____

If so, what will help me share them with someone I trust?

_____

_____

When do I find courage and strength to successfully talk about trauma in my life?

_____

_____

What does this prove about using power and control in helpful ways?

_____

_____

How can I use what I have learned about facing trauma to make healthy choices?

_____

_____

Staying Clear

Once you get in the habit of talking about trauma and not being afraid of it, you can learn to keep your mind clear so trauma echoes don't confuse you. First of all, you can learn to slow things down a bit. Trauma echoes can happen to anyone. They can happen when you least expect them. Sometimes you can predict when they might occur. They may try to throw you off balance, but you can learn to manage them in ways that no longer cause harm to yourself or others. This means you can learn to control them! They don't have to control you.

Another thing that can help you to take good care of yourself is to learn to keep the present clear when you have trauma echoes. *Staying clear simply means focusing on what is happening so you are aware the trauma is not really happening again*. This takes practice. You can learn to keep the present clear so trauma echoes are not so hard to deal with. Basically *it's a simple process of paying close attention to your thoughts, feelings, bodily reactions, and behavior when you have a trauma cue.*

When you figure out trauma cues you can learn to predict when you might have trauma echoes and prepare to manage them in healthy ways. You can learn to keep the present clear a lot easier when you allow people you trust to help out. When others know your trauma cues they can support you in a non-judgmental way through genuine warmth and empathy. *Empathy is the ability to share the feelings of another*. They can stay with you so you do not feel alone and isolated, or abandoned. They can do things with you, such as take a walk, so you can stay focused and feel safe.

Flashbacks, bad memories, nightmares and night terrors can make you feel like you are back at the time of the trauma. You may feel helpless and vulnerable.

Sylvia kept getting kicked out of class because the teacher got mad at her for daydreaming. When she told a counselor what was happening everyone realized daydreaming was not the problem at all. Sylvia was having trauma echoes in the classroom. She became nervous and started fidgeting. She drummed excitedly on the desk and disrupted class. Sylvia didn't realize she was doing those things. She was having flashbacks and thought she was back in a very scary situation. She didn't come out of a flashback until the teacher yelled and she realized she was being sent to the principal's office. Once Sylvia figured it out, she and the teacher worked together to reduce the trauma cues causing the flashbacks. She learned to slow her breathing down, pay attention to thoughts, feelings, how her body reacted, and her behavior in order to respond differently. Sylvia was then able to stay focused and remain in class.

You may feel as though you are back at the age when the bad thing happened. You're not! You're older now and have a lot more strength and resources than you did when it happened. You're bigger, you're smarter, and you know how to ask questions of people you trust so you can find your way to the answers. You also know how to get out of a bad situation that might cause more bad things to happen.

When you are able to recognize a trauma echo you can manage flashbacks, nightmares, or bad memories without confusing where you are, or what's going on. When you have an echo, hold on! If you feel a surge of tension in your body, grab the arm of a chair, a table, the hand of someone you trust, anything close by that is stable. Try to slow your breathing down as much as you can. Take deep breaths. If you're alone start by giving yourself messages to stay calm. Say nice things to yourself like "I can manage this", "this is old stuff, I can deal with it now", "hold on!" "slow down", or "it will pass". When you say things like this you're giving yourself courage and strength to face the pain.

If you are with someone you trust, think out loud. Say things like "oh no, the bad stuff is back", "here it comes, again" or something like that. Those things alert others to what's going on so they can help you through it. It's okay to share your fears. You might say how scared you are, or how scary it is to remember those things. When you have the courage to share your fear you may become less fearful. See if this works for you.

STAYING CLEAR

When am I successful managing trauma echoes without losing sense of where I am?

_____

_____

When I have a trauma echo how do I manage to keep my thoughts clear?

_____

_____

How does staying clear play a part in taking good care of myself?

_____

_____

What does this prove about using power and control in helpful ways?

_____

_____

How can I use what I have learned about staying clear to make healthy choices?

_____

_____

Top Ways to Stay Clear

_____

_____

_____

_____

_____

_____

_____

_____

_____

Attending to Pain

Attending to pain means accepting pain and facing it in a thoughtful way. Attending to pain means not making believe it will go away on its own. Some pain does not go away on its own so you have to learn how to manage it in healthy ways.

Trauma echoes can impact you in a lot of different ways at different times. They can be mild, or vague recollections; bad memories; or they can be very strong overwhelming reactions. Be prepared for all kinds of feelings and you'll be ready to manage even the toughest ones. Some feelings you can expect are sadness, fear, confusion, anger, loneliness, terror, and rage.

Ramon suffered beatings from his father until he was seventeen years old. He desperately wanted to be different than his father but he started hitting his girlfriend when she hurt his feelings or made him mad. He realized that arguments with his girlfriend brought up trauma echoes of his abuse. With the help of his counselor he created a safety plan for responding to both family and dating conflicts in new ways. He shared the plan with his family and girlfriend. The next time his father acted like he might hit him, Ramon excused himself and went for a bike ride as planned. He took off on his bike so he could control his nervous energy in solitude. He wanted time to calm down and think about the problem. Ramon later told his counselor that he rode about thirteen miles and was exhausted when he was done. He said it felt great to get out and have some time alone. Ramon talked about how powerful it felt to get away from his father's abuse and take good care of himself at the same time. He also learned to manage conflict with his girlfriend in respectful ways. Through family therapy, Ramon's dad learned to stop hitting him, and they both began practicing healthy ways to manage pain and anger.

You may feel overwhelmed and start crying. Let the tears come! The energy in your body can make you feel charged-up, or make you feel like running. Those feelings are knows as a fight or flight response. You may feel like curling up in a ball and hiding. Those reactions are known as shutting down, or freezing. These are normal reactions to trauma echoes. It's important to let the pain take its course without causing any harm. It will eventually let up. You may not believe it, but it will.

Think about how you can move your body in ways that don't cause harm. Practice controlling your breathing by slowing it down. After a while your body will slow itself down and you will know you successfully managed the pain. Your breathing will return to normal and you may find your body wanting to take some very deep breathes and let out a sigh. The agitation, or nervous energy eventually goes away, and you will be aware of what's around you. This is a good time to just relax.

All human beings need privacy and solitude. Solitude is being alone. It provides time and space to reflect and collect your thoughts when no one else is around.

As you learn to control trauma echoes you may find you want some private time to make sense of what's going on. You can let people know when you need solitude so they can help you have some time alone to simmer down.

There is a difference between being alone and isolation. Isolation means being set apart. Isolation can cause loneliness and confusion. Isolation might bring up fears and trauma echoes about neglect and abandonment. When you are alone you can tell whether solitude is helping, or hurting. If it's hurting look for someone you trust to talk to and be with. Learning the difference between isolation and solitude is an important part of taking good care of yourself. It can help you figure out how to respond to trauma echoes in healthy ways.

Just like loneliness, isolation can make people fearful of being alone. Fears like that can lead young people to make dangerous decisions. If someone is afraid to be alone they may go to any lengths to have a warm body close by. They may accept a physically and/or sexually abusive relationship, or decide to have a child long before they can take good care of a newborn. They may not protect themselves from harm.

ATTENDING TO PAIN

What new things am I learning about attending to my pain?

_____

_____

When do I successfully attend to my pain in healthy ways?

_____

_____

How might attending to my pain influence my sexual decision-making?

_____

_____

What does this tell me about my courage, strength and respect for myself?

_____

_____

How does attending to pain play a part in taking good care of myself?

_____

_____

It is only through attending to pain, and managing it in healthy ways, that people achieve health and well-being. Running away from it, or raging against it, prevent it from healing. Allowing it to run its course without causing harm helps people to go forward. You can do this in the following ways.

Top Ways to Attend to Pain Without Causing Harm

_____

_____

_____

_____

_____

_____

_____

_____

_____

_____

Expressing Honest Feelings

Depending on their impact, your body's response to trauma echoes can range from mildly irritating to overwhelming. By staying clear you can figure out how to stop trauma from continuing to cause harm. Learning to figure out painful feelings and to think clearly about them helps you express honest feelings in healthy ways.

The more you plan for trauma echoes, and practice managing them, the more successfully you can control them. Making sense of feelings that past trauma creates can help you gain even more control over them. Having a greater sense of control can help you feel competent and successful. Learning to identify and accept all the feelings you have allows you to face pain without fear and a desire to run away from it.

If you're alone when a trauma echo happens, you may want to write down your thoughts so you can come back to them as you make sense of the event. If you are with someone you trust you may want to talk with her, or him, about it. If you don't feel like talking right then, you can speak with someone later. You may want to rest for a while. Being flooded with emotions uses a lot of energy and takes a lot out of you. Resting after such an emotional time helps you calm down and relax. Resting allows your body to return to normal. You may be surprised by how strong you can feel after successfully managing pain.

If you need to make sense of it, find a safe place with someone you trust. This can help clear up any confusion about thoughts, feelings, and the impact on your body. You can get feedback about how you handled it, and plan for continued success in taking good care of yourself.

EXPRESSING HONEST FEELINGS

When do I successfully express painful feelings without causing harm?

_____

_____

How does expressing honest feelings help me take good care of myself?

_____

_____

What does this prove about my courage, strength and respect?

_____

_____

What does it say about using power, control and connection in helpful ways?

_____

_____

How can I use what I have learned about expressing feelings clearly to make healthy choices?

_____

_____

Top Ways to Express Honest Feelings

_____

_____

_____

_____

_____

_____

_____

_____

_____

_____

Self-Confidence

An important part of the trauma outcome process is self-confidence. *Self-confidence is believing in your ability to manage life's challenges and difficulties.* Taking good care of yourself results in self-confidence. It's about knowing you can handle things. Self-confidence is not something you achieve; it's something you practice every day. Bad things happen. *Self-confidence is trusting yourself to handle them well*.

When you believe you can handle a difficult or painful situation without causing harm, you build faith in yourself. Faith is unquestioning belief in something. It is complete trust and confidence. Faith takes a lot of practice! When you practice taking good care of yourself every day faith in yourself grows. You can develop faith in others and they build faith in you. You become stronger and stronger. You learn you can count on yourself to do good things and you build trust. People trust you and you can learn how to judge when others are trustworthy. You have unlimited opportunities to practice using power and control and connection with others in helpful ways. This is benevolence!

SELF-CONFIDENCE

What skills am I using to take good care of myself every day?

_____

_____

How do these skills help me build trust and faith in myself to gain self-confidence?

_____

_____

How can I use what I know about self-confidence to make healthy choices?

_____

_____

Top Ways to Build Self-Confidence

_____

_____

_____

_____

_____

_____

_____

_____

_____

Conclusion

WOW! Have you done a lot of work in this section! You have finished pages and pages of very important questions about healing and learning to take good care of yourself. Taking good care of yourself is a life-long journey. You live in a country that does not value taking good care of yourself. You are constantly getting messages to hurry, hurry, hurry; get with the program; stay on schedule; don't be late! You get messages to eat fast foods that are bad for you. And you get messages to buy, buy, buy, whether or not you need something. But you don't get many messages to slow down, be healthy, and enjoy well-being. You don't get many messages to be thoughtful about relationships so you can build intimate, safe connections with people who treat you respectfully. You don't get much information about how to express feelings so you can build faith in your abilities to manage them. You have this workbook so you get clear messages about learning to take good care of yourself.

Take a few minutes to think creatively about ways you can continue to practice taking good care of yourself. What messages do you want to give yourself to slow down? What clear messages about having fun do you want to remember? It may help to remember that some self-care is better, and more powerful, than others. For example, good nutrition and exercise are better for you in the long run than playing video games and watching television. Talking to friends and doing things together are much better than hanging around doing nothing and being bored. Sexual decisions that promote health and prevent unplanned or unwanted pregnancy are the best decisions you can make!

TAKING GOOD CARE OF MYSELF

What fun activities am I doing to take good care of myself ?

_____

_____

What other fun thing do I want to do?

_____

_____

What good decisions am I making about my sexuality?

_____

_____

Who supports, and encourages these decisions?

_____

_____

How can I use what I know about taking good care of myself to practice sexual health?

_____

_____

It's important to think about taking good care of yourself and there are many ways you can do so. Take some time to think about all the things you like to do and how they play a part in your health and well-being. Keeping yourself in good working condition can help you become the person you really want to be.

Top Ways I Can Take Good Care of Myself

_____

_____

_____

_____

_____

_____

_____

_____

_____

REFLECTIONS ON TAKING GOOD CARE OF MYSELF

How has it been helpful to answer questions about taking good care of myself?

_____

_____

What strengths am I learning about myself?

_____

_____

What are some of my favorite ways to take good care of myself?

_____

_____

What challenges am I facing in taking good care of myself?

_____

_____

Chapter Seven: Becoming the Person You Want to Be

Becoming the person you want to be is a unique challenge for everyone. You receive information all the time that influences decisions about who you want to be. You get a lot of messages telling you what kind of woman, or man you should be. It's impossible to figure out what kind of person you really want to be when past trauma is controlling your life. Decisions about health and well-being influence how you become the person you want to be.

When you make sense of your trauma outcome process and learn to control it you have a wonderful opportunity to begin figuring out who you really want to be. Since people are always changing this is something to think about your whole life. So the sooner you begin the sooner you'll be on your way!

Heroism

Facing pain and accepting feelings that come with it are the most important, and often most scary, part of healing. When you have courage and strength to manage such pain you take on a Herculean task. Hercules was a mythical person known to be very strong, powerful and courageous. *A Herculean task is one that is very difficult and requires great strength.* When a Herculean task is successfully completed a person can become a hero. *A hero is any person admired for his or her qualities or achievements, and regarded as an ideal or model.* Anyone who is able to face pain and despair without causing harm is a true hero!

Everyone who is able to cry when he or she feels intense pain may be facing a Herculean task. Since boys are taught that tears are bad, and a

Top 10 Reasons For Becoming The Person You Want To Be

1. Experience kindness and affection
2. Enjoy loving relationships
3. Control your own life
4. Use your brain thoughtfully
5. Use benevolent power
6. Have freedom to do what you want
7. Have fun
8. Live long and prosper
9. Make the world a better place
10. Allow your spirit to soar!

sign of weakness, it can very hard for young men to believe the opposite. Some young women are afraid of crying too. Some people are afraid that if they start crying they will never stop. Tears usually last a short time. As pain goes away so do tears.

Tears are extremely important in healing. Tears are a body's way of releasing pain. There's nothing shameful about them. They are simply a part of body functions. When tear ducts don't work properly it causes problems and requires medical attention. Everyone experiences pain in life and crying in response to that pain helps it heal faster and more completely. We should never miss a good opportunity to cry! We need to cry about the pain there is in our world.

An unsung hero is one whose courage and strength may not be celebrated. Because others may not know how hard it is to manage your pain, you may be an unsung hero. There are a lot of unsung heroes in our world. I hope your courage to face pain in healthy ways is honored and celebrated by people who care about you. Whenever you attend to your pain in this way you are taking excellent care of yourself.

HEROISM

What helps me to face a Herculean task?

_____

_____

When am I being heroic?

_____

_____

Who comes to mind when I think of a heroic person?

_____

_____

How do they show their heroism?

_____

_____

How can I use what I have learned about heroism to make healthy choices?

_____

_____

How can heroism help me to become the person I want to be?

_____

_____

Top Things I'm Learning About Heroism

_____
_____
_____
_____
_____
_____
_____
_____
_____

Empathy and Compassion

Empathy is the ability to share in the feelings another. When you are able to understand the full impact that trauma has on victims, including yourself, you are able to consider true empathy. Empathy can help you to understand how pain in life influences thoughts, feelings, and behavior.

When you understand empathy, it can play a powerful role in your health and well-being. Thinking of others allows people to consider benevolence and compassion. *Compassion is sorrow for the sufferings or trouble of another, accompanied by an urge to help.* When you connect your feelings about trauma with similar feelings in others, you can think differently about how you want to behave.

When Jamie was little she had no one to protect her from abuse. Her mother had a mental illness and she never knew her dad. She said the worst part was not having a dad, so she got to know a neighbor, Mike, who was very nice to her and invited her to be a part of his family whenever she was able. After her mother's parental rights were terminated, she was in different foster homes but was able to connect with the other family every now and then. That connection helped her get through the hard parts and she learned empathy and compassion from her neighbor and his family. Mike, and his family taught her how to treat others with respect and care, and Jamie learned a lot about helping others.

Instead of hurting you may find you want to help, both yourself and others. A lot of healing starts with helping others. You might find you want to help yourself first. Empathy and compassion can be contagious. It doesn't matter where you start. It just matters that you start. Developing empathy and compassion for yourself will help you to consider practicing empathy and compassion for others.

What was the worst part of any trauma you had? What did you really need when bad things were happening to you? I'll bet you needed love, and to be cared for. A hug and comforting words help people manage pain. Everyone needs others to turn to when times are tough. Everyone needs comfort and compassion. A hand to hold and someone to talk to are some of the best gifts in life. Empathy and compassion lead to benevolence.

EMPATHY AND COMPASSION

When am I treated with empathy and compassion?

_____

_____

How do empathy and compassion comfort me?

_____

_____

When do I show empathy and compassion?

_____

_____

How do empathy and compassion play a part in making healthy choices?

_____

_____

How can I use what I know about empathy and compassion to become the person I want to be?

_____

_____

Top Ways to Practice Empathy and Compassion

_____

_____

_____

_____

_____

_____

_____

_____

_____

Making Amends

Making amends is taking responsibility for hurting others, and making a commitment to stop it. To make amends is to do something to make up for injury, loss, or damage that someone has caused. Most people want to make amends when they hurt someone. Making amends is not just apologizing. It is apologizing AND stopping all harmful behavior. Making amends comes from empathy and compassion, and is heroic and honorable. When others make amends for causing harm it is a gift that may help victims heal and forgive. If you're not around people who hurt you in the past, they may not be able to make amends. You can still heal from abuse when others don't make amends for hurting you, or not protecting you. When you have caused harm, making amends reflects your success in overcoming pain and anger. It shows you want to become a good person.

Making amends happens in a variety of different ways. The most powerful ways to make amends is to take full responsibility for causing any pain and to apologize to anyone who was hurt by violence or abuse. This takes a lot of courage! Apologizing is an act of great honor!

MAKING AMENDS

When have others made amends to me?

_____

_____

When do I have the courage to make amends for causing harm?

_____

_____

How does it help people to heal?

_____

_____

How can I use what I know about making amends to make healthy choices?

_____

_____

How is the strength, courage and honor to make amends helping me become the person I want to be?

_____

_____

Top Things
I'm Learning About
Making Amends

_____

_____

_____

_____

_____

_____

_____

_____

Forgiveness

To forgive is to give up resentment or the desire to punish. It is the ability to let go of anger. Deciding to forgive can influence health and well-being. Just like other things in this workbook, forgiveness takes practice. Forgiveness can be a Herculean task. It can be very hard to forgive someone who hurt you deeply. Forgiveness is very hard work. Sometimes it can be done and sometimes it can't.

Some people say you should forgive and forget, but trauma is seldom forgotten. Most people simply learn to live with memories of trauma. When you are strong and courageous you work hard to prevent the memories from causing any harm. This is the decision to heal pain.

There is an old saying that "to err is human, to forgive is divine." What a powerful statement! Everybody makes mistakes, but it takes greatness to be able to forgive. Wow! This is one tall order! How do you learn to rise above pain to forgive those who hurt you? How do people you have hurt, rise above their pain, to forgive you? You can figure this out and go on to become the person you want to be.

Many bad things that happen in life are no one's fault. Forgiveness comes easier when no one is at fault. When someone you love dies it is extremely painful. If you are afraid to feel the intense pain of such a loss you might try to hide it by acting angry with doctors or nurses who couldn't keep that person alive. When you are able to face the pain you realize death is not usually anyone's fault. As you let go of the desire to punish the medical staff, the anger goes away and you can forgive them for not being able to save your loved one.

If you believe in God, you may be angry that God took your loved one away from you. Sometimes people in pain blame God and have to take some time to figure out how they will practice forgiveness. If you feel badly about something you did you might be blaming yourself, and turning your anger inward against yourself. Sharing such thoughts with someone you trust can help you forgive yourself.

Some trauma may be the fault of someone who mistreated you. It may be difficult to consider forgiving them. If they are sorry for what they have done, apologize, and made amends, it might be easier to forgive them. It still takes some work. It can take a long time to forgive people who hurt you.

Unfortunately many people who hurt others don't apologize or receive punishment for harm they caused. When people who hurt you don't make amends it can play a part in your health and well-being. It may seem very unfair if you are struggling while people who hurt you haven't paid for what they did. Life is very unfair at times. Just because life is unfair doesn't mean it's okay for others to get away with causing harm, especially when it's a crime.

It can be really hard to even consider forgiving such people! It also makes sense that the pain they caused got worse from anger and resentment that came from knowing they were not held accountable for the harm. That's a lot of righteous anger! Righteous means having a legitimate right to something. In this case it means you have a right to be angry about such injustice.

So how do you learn to practice forgiveness when you have had such awful experiences? This can be a tough one!

FORGIVENESS

What things happened to me that I have not forgiven others for?

_____

_____

What is preventing me from forgiving them?

_____

_____

What things do I want to be forgiven for?

_____

_____

When am I able to forgive?

_____

_____

Who do I want to forgive me?

_____

_____

What do I need to do to earn their forgiveness?

_____

_____

What things do I need to forgive myself for?

_____

_____

How can I use what I know about forgiveness to make healthy choices?

_____

_____

How can forgiveness play a part in helping me become the person I want to be?

_____

_____

Top Things I'm Learning About Forgiveness

_____

_____

_____

_____

_____

_____

_____

_____

_____

Honor and Integrity

Honor is giving respect, earning a good reputation, and having a strong sense of what is right and what is wrong. You may be surprised to develop a sense of honor. It is about daring to take a stand to become the best person you can be. *Integrity is a big word that comes from acting with honor.* When you treat yourself and others with respect and care, you are acting with honor and integrity. People look up to you, respect you, and admire you. You learn to respect and honor yourself. You can stand tall instead of cowering and running away from problems and the pain that they cause. You can make healthy choices even when they are hard because you know that risky or harmful behavior is not in your best interest.

When you embrace honor and integrity you can decide what kind of person you want to be, and you can become that person! You can learn to make decisions based upon desire to be good to yourself. Being good to yourself also helps you to be good to others.

HONOR AND INTEGRITY

Who comes to mind when I think of a person of honor and integrity?

_____

_____

How do they show it?

_____

_____

When do I behave with honor and integrity?

_____

_____

What does this prove about me as a person?

_____

_____

Demitri decided to become an honest man and work to pay for his own apartment and food. He wanted to learn how to date girls and he hoped to fall in love and have a family. Soon after he left residential treatment he got a job and works full time. He doesn't want to become a parent until he can provide a good life for his children. He knows he can't until he's older and can do more for them.

Jenna really wants to get pregnant and have a baby even though she's in her teens. While she believes she can be a better parent than hers ever were, she knows what it's like growing up on welfare and never having enough of what she needs. Still, she really wants someone to love and who will be with her all the time. Jenna doesn't have a steady boyfriend and doesn't think she's pretty enough to keep one. She struggles in school but is working with her case manager to get tutoring and a mentor. She's thinking about waiting to get pregnant if she finds some friends to hang out with and have fun. She knows she needs to find some love in her life. She's beginning to understand that having a baby so young may be harder than she thinks. The idea of having some fun in life after all the pain of her childhood is sounding good. She's moved around so much she never had long lasting friends to love. Maybe now that she's settling down she can do it!

What part are honor and integrity playing in helping me to become the person I want to be?

_____

_____

Figuring out what kind of person you want to be helps you stay focused on goals and dreams. All the effort you've put into this workbook can help you do this. Becoming the person you want to be is a daily challenge to behave in ways that help you feel good about life and living.

WHAT KIND OF PERSON DO I WANT TO BE?

What am I good at?

_____

_____

What things do I like and want to do?

_____

_____

What comes to mind when I think of the kind of person I want to be?

_____

_____

How do my sexual decisions play a part in become the person I want to be?

_____

_____

When am I successfully being the person I want to be?

_____

_____

How is this new information helping me make healthy choices?

_____

_____

Top Ways I Can Become The Person I Want to Be

_____

_____

_____

_____

_____

_____

_____

Conclusion

You're almost there! You have done incredible work making sense of your life and thinking about the future you want to create for yourself. You're learning how to become the master of your destiny! *Destiny is events that will happen in the future. To master something is to rule or govern, to become expert at it.* To become a master of your destiny is to be clear about what you want in life so you can take control to get there.

REFLECTION ON BECOMING THE PERSON I WANT TO BE

How is it helpful to figure out what kind of person I want to be?

_____

_____

What have I learned about myself from these questions?

_____

_____

How am I daring to take a stand to become the person I want to be?

_____

_____

Chapter Eight:
Pursuing My Dreams

There is no failure except in no longer trying.

— Elbert Hubbard

Earlier in the workbook you answered some questions about your dreams. All human beings have dreams. Not everyone has the courage and strength to pursue those dreams and make them a reality. Not all dreams come true but it is exciting to work towards them!

The reason you had questions about dreams earlier in the workbook was to help you think about things that might help you look towards the future. Dreams can have a very strong influence on your life. When you create dreams that reflect your hopes and desires and hold on to them, you are much more likely to make them come true. Being clear about your dreams can help you prepare for opportunities to pursue them. Telling people you trust about your dreams can help them support you in making your dreams come true.

Making healthy choices can help you pursue dreams you would not have been able to before. Trauma can get in the way of pursuing dreams. You can dare to take a stand for yourself and spend time making your dreams come true.

This can be serious fun! There is nothing more fun than living the life you really want to live. There will always be bad things that happen, and trauma in the world, but when you embark on a journey to fulfill your dreams there is nothing more exciting. When you decide to pursue your dreams it can be helpful to make a list.

DREAMS I HAVE ABOUT …

Taking good care of myself?

_____

_____

Becoming the person I want to be?

_____

_____

Loving relationships?

_____

_____

Talents I want to develop?

_____

_____

Having fun?

_____

_____

Now that you have thought some more about dreams, please go back to the section in this workbook on dreams. It is on page 14. Take a look at your answers and then come back to this page.

PURSUING MY DREAMS

How have any of my dreams changed since beginning this workbook?

_____

_____

What new dreams do I have?

_____

_____

What do my dreams tell me about making healthy choices?

_____

_____

How have all these questions helped me to be more clear about my dreams?

_____

_____

How will my dreams help me become the person I want to be?

_____

_____

Some dreams come easy and some dreams take a long time to come true. Think about your dreams and place them in the order in which you might pursue them.

Finally, take each dream and answer the following questions about each one.

Top Ways to Pursue My Dreams

_____

_____

_____

_____

_____

_____

_____

_____

Dream Number One: _____

What do I want, and need, to make this dream come true?

_____

Who can help me make this dream come true?

_____

How long do I think it will take to make this one come true?

_____

How will it help me to become the person I want to be?

_____

Dream Number Two: _____

What do I want, and need, to make this dream come true?

_____

Who can help me make this dream come true?

_____

How long do I think it will take to make this one come true?

_____

How will it help me to become the person I want to be?

_____

The Order In Which I Can Pursue These Dreams

_____

_____

_____

_____

_____

_____

_____

_____

_____

Dream Number Three: _____

What do I want, and need, to make this dream come true?

_____

Who can help me make this dream come true?

_____

How long do I think it will take to make this one come true?

_____

How will it help me to become the person I want to be?

_____

Dream Number Four: _____

What do I want, and need, to make this dream come true?

_____

Who can help me make this dream come true?

_____

How long do I think it will take to make this one come true?

_____

How will it help me to become the person I want to be?

_____

Dream Number Five: _____

What do I want, and need, to make this dream come true?

_____

Who can help me make this dream come true?

_____

How long do I think it will take to make this one come true?

_____

How will it help me to become the person I want to be?

_____

Dream Number Six: _____

What do I want, and need, to make this dream come true?

_____

Who can help me make this dream come true?

_____

How long do I think it will take to make this one come true?

_____

How will it help me to become the person I want to be?

_____

Dream Number Seven: _____

What do I want, and need, to make this dream come true?

_____

Who can help me make this dream come true?

_____

How long do I think it will take to make this one come true?

_____

How will it help me to become the person I want to be?

_____

Dream Number Eight: _____

What do I want, and need, to make this dream come true?

_____

Who can help me make this dream come true?

_____

How long do I think it will take to make this one come true?

_____

How will it help me to become the person I want to be?

_____

Dream Number Nine: _____

What do I want, and need, to make this dream come true?

_____

Who can help me make this dream come true?

_____

How long do I think it will take to make this one come true?

_____

How will it help me to become the person I want to be?

_____

Dream Number Ten: _____

What do I want, and need, to make this dream come true?

_____

Who can help me make this dream come true?

_____

How long do I think it will take to make this one come true?

_____

How will it help me to become the person I want to be?

_____

Conclusion

Finishing this workbook gives you an opportunity to practice things you learned for the rest of your life. All human beings have the same challenge. Pursuing your dreams takes courage and persistence. *Persistence means continuing over a long period of time*. Persistence in making healthy choices can help you think about your life differently.

The trauma outcome process is something you can use for the rest of your life. It helps everyone understand harmful behavior that causes problems in life. You have done remarkable work making sense of your life. You have completed a Herculean task!

REFLECTIONS ON PURSUING MY DREAMS

How has it been helpful to answer questions about my dreams?

_____

Who has helped me the most with all this stuff?

_____

How will I stay connected to them in the future?

_____

What have I learned about myself that will help me keep making healthy choices?

_____

How will I plan for continued success?

_____

You have covered a lot of ground in this workbook! You've spent a lot of time thinking about things like strength and courage and respect. You've thought about how others treat you and how you treat others. You've answered a lot of questions about power and control and connection. You've had a lot of things to figure out about pain and decisions about healing that pain.

Connection may be the most powerful force in the universe. Everything in nature is connected and you are part of it. Successful people rely on other trustworthy people. It is important to keep people like this in your life. You can't do it alone.

Sometimes people you connect with are not good for you. Staying connected with them may not be in your best interest. There might be people you have been close to who have influenced decisions to behave in harmful ways. Such people are not trustworthy. Unless they have already made significant changes to stop causing harm it may not be safe to continue connecting with them. Even though you may love these people you may have to make healthy choices to protect yourself from them. This can be hard, but you can do it. You can learn to love them from afar. You can love them and know it's not safe to be around them. It is sad when you have to do this, but it is much better than accepting harm in your life.

It is very important to realize there are other people who will love you in healthy ways. Their names and addresses are on this page. Keep this page or a copy of it with you so you can contact them whenever you need to. Stay connected with these people! They will be there for you. And you can be there for them.

Even though she wasn't a great student, Carmen decided education would be her way out of poverty. She made some poor decisions as a teenager and had unprotected sex a few times. She was very lucky she didn't get any infections, and she didn't get pregnant. During her first year in college she went to a sexual health clinic for her first exam and never took any risks again. It took her eight years to finish college. She dropped out of school to get married when she was twenty, but the marriage didn't work out. She went back to school and got married a second time when she was almost 26. She had a baby when she was twenty-eight. She had dreams to be the best wife and mother she could be. She also had dreams to become a doctor to help children. She never achieved her dream to become a doctor but she works hard every day to help abused children. She also thinks every day about being the best person she can be. She loves to read, watch movies, and ride her bike, and makes sure to have fun every day! She loves many people and feels loved by family, friends and co-workers.

PEOPLE I CAN TRUST TO SUPPORT MY SUCCESS

Name: _____ Phone Number: _____

Name: _____ Phone Number: _____

Name: _____ Phone Number: _____

Name: _____ Phone Number: _____

Name: _____ Phone Number: _____

Of all the work you've done which parts of this workbook do you think will help you the most? Please write these things down so they will stay with you and continue to help you along life's journey. Make sure you share them with people you trust so that they can continue to support your success and celebrate your life!

Become the person you want to be and have fun along the way!

Top Things I've Learned About Health and Well-Being

_____

_____

_____

_____

_____

_____

_____

_____

_____

_____

Resources

For more information the following websites have more information about sexual health:

www.plannedparenthood.org

www.siecus.org

www.sexedlibrary.org

www.guttmacher.org

www.advocatesforyouth.org

www.answer.rutgers.edu

www.thenationalcampaign.org

Get resources for gay and lesbian youth at:

www.lambda.org

www.advocatesforyouth.org

www.amplifyyourvoice.org

www.lgbthealth.net

www.thegyc.com

www.nyacyouth.org

Glossary of Terms

Abuse: repeated cruelty towards people or animals.

Acquaintance, Friendship, or Date Rape: see definition on page 23.

Admirable: deserving respect and approval.

Affection: expression of fond, or tender feelings.

Aggression: any forceful, attacking behavior.

Amends: something given, or done, to make up for injury or loss.

Anger: a strong feeling of being upset.

Arousal: a response to a stimulus.

Attraction: causing interest or pleasure.

Benevolent: kind and good.

Benevolent Power: a force for good used to make things better and to benefit people.

Bi-Sexual: being sexually attracted to both sexes.

Child Sexual Abuse: see definition on page 22.

Compassion: Compassion is sorrow for the sufferings or trouble of another, accompanied by an urge to help.

Coercion: see definition on page 23.

Complex: having many different but connected parts.

Confidential: showing trust in another; entrusted with private matters.

Connection: attachment by ties of affection or devotion; joining together with, and relation between things; an influential person through whom one can get special favors.

Consensual Sexual Intimacy: sexual activity based upon agreement.

Control: to exercise authority over, to direct, or command.

Courage: being able to deal with anything that's difficult.

Cruelty: behavior that causes pain and suffering

Destiny: events that will happen in the future.

Discrimination: unjust treatment.

Dreams: fond hopes and desires.

Emotional Abuse: causing hurt feelings that prevent victims from being able to take good care of themselves.

Embarrassment: feeling self-conscious or awkward.

Emotional: having to do with feelings.

Empathy: the ability to share in another's emotions or feelings.

Fantasies: unfulfilled desires; thoughts about doing something you think you might like to do but normally would not do.

Flirtation: playing at love.

Forgiveness: to give up resentment or the desire to punish.

Gender Messages: things you are taught to believe about what it means to be a man or woman.

Genuine: being who you really are: sincere and honest and true.

Hazing: see definition on page 23.

Heal: to make well, as in the word healthy.

Herculean Task: activity that is very difficult and requires great strength.

Hero: any person admired for his or her qualities or achievements, and regarded as an ideal or model.

Heroism: acts of courage and strength that help people.

Heterosexual: sexual attraction between people of the opposite sex.

Homosexual: sexual attraction between people of the same sex.

Honor: giving respect, earning a good reputation, and having a strong sense of what is right and what is wrong.

Identity: the fact of being who a person is.

Integrity: acting with honor.

Intimate: private or personal.

Love: a deep and tender feeling of attachment.

Making Amends: taking responsibility for hurting others, and making a commitment to stop it.

Masturbation: stimulating your own genitals for the purpose of sexual pleasure.

Mutilation: means to damage or injure.

Negative Self-Talk: telling yourself bad things about yourself.

Neglect: to fail to care for properly.

Offending Acts: criminal acts that get you in trouble with the law.

Outcome: a result or consequence.

Persistence: continuing over a long period of time.

Physical: having to do with the body.

Physical Abuse: hurting a person's body.

Poverty: not having enough of things that you need.

Power: an ability to do something, to exert force or energy.

Prejudice: negative judgment about people that cause harm.

Private: concerning a particular person; not intended for the public.

Process: a particular way of doing something.

Reaction: a feeling, or action in response to something. It is an action brought on by resistance to another action.

Respect: showing concern for the feelings, wishes, or rights of others.

Repressed Feelings: to keep down or hold back, to control so strictly as to prevent natural expression.

Reproduction: the process by which humans, animals and plants create new individuals.

Resentment: feeling bitter about being treated unfairly.

Revenge: hurting someone for something mean they did to you.

Revenge Fantasies: a desire to get back at someone and hurt them.

Secrecy: to hide something.

Self-Confidence: believing in your ability to manage life's challenges and difficulties.

Sex: the character of being male or female; anything connected with sexual pleasure.

Sex roles: messages that give you ideas about your role as a male or female.

Sexual: anything involving sex.

Sexual Abuse: using another person for personal sexual needs.

Sexual Aggression: anytime sex is used to hurt someone.

Sexual Arousal: a body's physical response to something that stimulates sexual feelings.

Sexual Harassment: see definition on page 23.

Sexual Harm: is any sexual act that hurts someone, or any sexual act that is illegal.

Sexual Intercourse: the sexual joining of two individuals; one way of engaging in sexual behavior.

Sexual Pleasure: anything someone finds to be sexually enjoyable, delightful and satisfying.

Sexual Stimulation, or Arousal: a body's physical response to something that brings on sexual feelings.

Sexuality: everything about you that makes you who you are, not just your sexual behavior.

Shame: painful feelings caused by bad behavior

Staying Clear: focusing on what is happening so you are aware trauma is not really happening again. It's a simple process of paying close attention to thoughts, feelings, bodily reactions, and behavior when having a trauma cue.

Strength: having the power to get something done.

Taking Good Care of Yourself: protecting yourself, and others, from harm.

Teasing: annoying, or harassing by mocking or poking fun.

Telling: reporting information to get help.

Thinking Errors: information that causes you to think in ways that are not correct.

Transgender: to identify with a gender other than the one (male or female) they were born with.

Trauma: a very painful experience that has a lasting effect on your life.

Trauma Cues: a signal from one, or more of your senses that sets off a response to past trauma.

Trauma Echoes: thoughts, feelings and bodily reactions that imitate past trauma and keep coming back, or repeating parts of it.

Trauma Outcome Process: the way you choose to deal with bad things that happened to you.

Verbal Abuse: saying hurtful things that cause others to feel badly about themselves.

Violence: physical force intended to hurt, damage, or kill someone, or something.

Vulnerable: open to being wounded or easily hurt.

Well-being: the state of being comfortable, healthy, or happy.